Free at Last

THE SECOND MADAM & EVE COLLECTION

By S. Francis, H. Dugmore & Rico

PENGUIN BOOKS

PENGUIN BOOKS

Published by the Penguin Group
27 Wrights Lane, London W8 5TZ, England
Viking Penguin, a division of Penguin Books USA Inc,
375 Hudson Street, New York, New York 10014, USA
Penguin Books Australia Ltd, Ringwood, Victoria, Australia
Penguin Books Canada Ltd, 10 Alcorn Avenue, Toronto, Ontario, Canada M4V 3B2
Penguin Books (NZ) Ltd, 182-190 Wairau Road, Auckland 10, New Zealand
Penguin Books, Amethyst Street, Theta Ext 1, Johannesburg, South Africa

Penguin Books Ltd, Registered Offices: Harmondsworth, Middlesex, England

First published by Penguin Books 1994

ISBN 0-140-24833-1

Reproduction by Positive Proof
Printed and bound by Creda Press

MADAM&EVE

"AT LAST, IT'S TIME FOR A LAUGH."
"People of all colours and political stripe
can't get enough of Madam & Eve."
– Newsweek Magazine

**"MADAM & EVE... HAS LOCATED A
COMMON NATIONAL FUNNYBONE."**
"...Holds a mirror up to a divided society and
draws laughter from both sides of the fence."
– The Washington Post

"CARTOON OF THE YEAR."
"Plasters grins on our faces, makes us giggle
and side with the victorious underdog."
– Cosmopolitan Magazine

**"THESE TWO WOMEN HAVE CAPTURED
A NEW NICHE IN POPULAR CULTURE."**
– The New York Times

"MADAM & EVE FOR PRESIDENT."
"Scores high on the hilarity barometer...
fortified with liberal doses of political realism."
– Weekly Mail & Guardian

"CARTOONISTS OF THE YEAR."
"A humorous and often ironic look at South African
society through the eyes of a rich suburban
housewife and her liberated maid."
– The Weekend Star

"A STARTLING SUCCESS."
– The Guardian, UK

"DOWNRIGHT HILARIOUS."
"Madam & Eve is a bridge over which a good
chuckle can roll until the belly-laughs at our
idiosyncrasies eventually are allowed
free transport."
– The Cape Times

"DELIGHTFUL AND DELICIOUSLY IRONIC."
"Madam & Eve's creators clearly have their
fingers spot on the pulse of South Africa life.
It's a collector's item."
– The Citizen

**"MADAM & EVE TICKLES THE FUNNYBONE
OF SOUTH AFRICA."**
"A humorous and often ironic look at South African
society through the eyes of a rich suburban
housewife and her liberated maid."
– The Weekend Star

KNOCK! KNOCK!

TAKE US TO YOUR LEADER.

WE DON'T HAVE ONE YET. CAN YOU COME BACK APRIL 27th?

© Rapid Phase Entertainment · 1993

EARTHLING—WE **DEMAND** THAT YOU TAKE US TO YOUR LEADER.

COME BACK IN EIGHT MONTHS.

EIGHT MONTHS?

YES. WE'RE HAVING OUR FIRST **ELECTION!**

AND AFTER THE ELECTION, THEN CAN YOU TAKE US TO YOUR LEADER?

NO. THEN I CAN TAKE YOU TO OUR **INTERIM** LEADER.

© Rapid Phase Entertainment · 1993

LET'S GET OUT OF HERE. THESE PEOPLE ARE NUTS.

MADAM!! THERE'S TWO **ALIENS** AT THE DOOR!

FROM MOZAMBIQUE?

ACTUALLY, WE'RE FROM THE PLANET XYBORG.

THEY'RE FROM XYBORG!

© Rapid Phase Entertainment · 1993

IS THAT **NEAR** MOZAMBIQUE?

5

I THINK WE UNDERSTAND NOW. "*APARTHEID*" IS WHEN WHITE EARTHLINGS DEMAND TO STAY COMPLETELY **SEPARATE** FROM BLACK EARTHLINGS.

YES.

...AND THEN WE MOVE INTO THEIR HOMES, WORK FOR THEM AND RAISE THEIR CHILDREN.

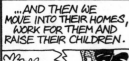

RUN THAT BY US ONE MORE TIME.

SO... MANY OF YOUR PROBLEMS ARE CAUSED BY RACIAL INTOLERANCE.

I GUESS SO.

AN EXPERIMENT?

GOOD IDEA. SET THE TRANSFORMER RAY.

ZZAP!

AAAAAAH!

INTERESTING REACTION.

THIS PLACE YOU CALL "SOUTH AFRICA" HAS NO REDEEMING QUALITIES! GIVE US **ONE** GOOD REASON WHY WE SHOULDN'T **DESTROY** YOU!

THERE'S **LOTS** OF REASONS!

NAME ONE.

... HAVE YOU TRIED **BILTONG**?

MADAM & Eve

BY S. FRANCIS, H. DUGMORE & RICO.

EVE! DON'T FORGET-- YOU HAVEN'T WASHED THE DISHES!

YES, MADAM.

MARIA! DON'T FORGET-- YOU HAVEN'T WASHED THE DISHES!

YES, MADAM.

WHO WAS **THAT**?

THAT'S MARIA. I ALWAYS WONDERED WHAT IT'S LIKE TO BE A **MADAM**, SO I HIRED MY OWN MAID FOR A WEEK.

YOU HIRED YOUR OWN MAID! THAT'S THE MOST **OUTRAGEOUS** THING I EVER HEARD OF!

WHY? THE WORK GETS DONE.

MADAM!

YES?

ALRIGHT, THAT **DOES** IT! THERE'S ONLY ROOM ENOUGH FOR **ONE** MADAM IN THIS HOUSE-- ME! TELL YOUR "MAID" SHE'S GOT TO GO!

OKAY, MADAM. YOU WIN. BUT AT LEAST PAY HER FOR THE WHOLE WEEK.

FINE.

⟨ A WEEK'S PAY... FOR ONLY A HOUR'S WORK. ⟩

⟨ YOU'RE A GENIUS, COUSIN EVE. ⟩

⟨ I KNOW. SAY HI TO UNCLE JOE. ⟩

© Rapid Phase Entertainment 1993

MADAM & Eve

BY S. FRANCIS, H. DUGMORE & RICO

HMMM... DUSTBINS FULL OF RUBBISH... FUZZBALLS ON THE RUG... DIRTY WINDOWS... THIS LOOKS LIKE A JOB FOR...

SUPERMAID!

USING HER POWERS OF **SUPER-SPEED**, SUPERMAID CLEANS THE LOUNGE IN MERE SECONDS!

AND YET, NO ONE WOULD SUSPECT THAT **SUPERMAID** IS ACTUALLY **EVE**... A MILD-MANNERED AND SEEMINGLY LAZY DOMESTIC MAINTENANCE ASSISTANT!

EVE! HAVE YOU DONE THE WASHING YET?!

UH-OH! THAT VOICE! IT CAN ONLY BE ONE PERSON... MY ARCH-NEMESIS... THE FIENDISH DOCTOR MADAM!

YOU CAN START WITH THE PILLOW-CASES. I LEFT THE **OMO** ON THE COUNTER.

A TRAP!!

≡GASP≡ "OMO-ITE!" SUPERMAID'S ONE **WEAKNESS!** ≡CHOKE≡ FEEL WEAK... DIZZY...

... GOT TO REST... AND RECHARGE MY POWERS...

EVE! ARE YOU SLACKING OFF **AGAIN**?! HONESTLY... YOU'RE THE LAZIEST MAID I'VE EVER SEEN!!

LUCKILY, MY **SECRET IDENTITY** IS STILL SAFE.

11

WAIT TILL I TELL THE NEIGHBOURS THE STAR OF "JURASSIC PARK" IS IN MY HOUSE.

DO YOU KNOW STEVEN SPIELBERG?

KNOW HIM!? THE ☆✆#6☆!! STILL OWES ME A WEEK'S PAY.

NOT TO MENTION ALL THE DINOSAUR **MERCHANDISE**! MY PICTURE'S ON T-SHIRTS, LUNCH BOXES AND BED SPREADS! DO YOU THINK I GET A PERCENTAGE? **NO**!!

I TELL YOU, IT MAKES ME SO MAD, I COULD JUST **EAT** SOMEBODY.

MADAM??

SO...YOU'RE HERE TO PROMOTE "JURASSIC PARK."

YEAH...I'LL BE DOING GOOD MORNING SOUTH AFRICA... PICK'N'PAY APPEARANCES... STUFF LIKE THAT.

ARE YOU **REAL** OR A SPECIAL EFFECT COMPUTER IMAGE?

GO AHEAD. TAKE A CLOSER LOOK.

ROAAR

I LOVE THIS JOB.

SO, STEVEN SPIELBERG ISN'T GIVING YOU A PIECE OF ALL THE "JURASSIC PARK" MERCHANDISE?

NO...THE CHEAPSKATE.

BUT **WAIT** TILL THEY MAKE THE SEQUEL! MY AGENT'S GONNA GET ME A REAL **SWEET** DEAL.

I MEAN, WHO ELSE ARE THEY GONNA GET TO PLAY ME? DE NIRO!? NICHOLSON!? **HA**!!

...OF COURSE, WHAT I REALLY WANT TO DO... IS "**DIRECT**."

MADAM & Eve

BY S. FRANCIS, H. DUGMORE & RICO.

OKAY EVE... I'LL PAY YOUR TUITION... BUT IF YOU **WIN** ONE DAY, WE SPLIT THE CASH AND PRIZES!

DEAL!

THE **ANC** SCHOOL OF BEAUTY PAGEANTS

...YOU WON'T BE SORRY, MADAM.

HI. WELCOME TO THE ANC SCHOOL OF BEAUTY PAGEANTS. CAN I HELP YOU?

WHAT DO I GET IF I SIGN UP FOR YOUR "BEGINNER'S CLASS"?

FIRST, YOU RECEIVE AN IMITATION-DIAMOND CROWN, A SASH AND A SKIMPY COSTUME. THEN OUR PANEL OF TRAINED **ANC BEAUTY EXPERTS** GIVE YOU AN HONEST APPRAISAL OF HOW YOU LOOK IN A SWIMSUIT AND HIGH HEELS.

NEXT, YOU'LL BE A PART OF PETER MOKABA'S INTENSIVE WORKSHOP ON POISE, CHARM AND TACT.

AND FINALLY, YOU'LL LEARN HOW TO ANSWER TOUGH QUESTIONS ABOUT "WORLD PEACE" AND THE ENVIRONMENT IN ONLY TWO SENTENCES.

WAIT A MINUTE! I'VE HEARD THESE BEAUTY PAGEANTS ARE **FIXED**!

© Rapid Phase Entertainment · 1993

NOT ANY MORE! SINCE **WE'VE** GOTTEN INVOLVED, IT'S STRICTLY "ONE JUDGE, ONE BALLOT."

GREAT! WHEN CAN I START?

RIGHT NOW! EVEN AS WE SPEAK, ANC OFFICIALS OF THE **HIGHEST** LEVEL ARE OFFERING ADVICE TO A GROUP OF STUDENT CONTESTANTS!

EXCUSE ME, TOKYO... BUT SHOULD I GO WITH THE BIKINI... OR THE TUBE TOP?

TOUGH CHOICE. I VOTE FOR THE BIKINI... CYRIL?

13

OUR TOPIC TONIGHT IS THE NEW PETROL PRICE. SO PLEASE WELCOME MY NEXT GUEST--WHO'S BEEN DESCRIBED AS "IRREFUTABLY STUBBORN". ENERGY AFFAIRS MINISTER GEORGE BARTLETT.

UH, MINISTER... YOU'RE SUPPOSED TO SIT **NEXT** TO THE PRESENTER...

WELL, I WANT TO SIT **HERE!**

BUT...YOU'RE OUT OF CAMERA RANGE.

I DON'T **CARE! THIS** IS THE SEAT I'VE CHOSEN. CASE **CLOSED.**

MINISTER... PLEASE--

NO! NO! NO! I ABSOLUTELY **REFUSE** TO BUDGE!

MY GUEST TONIGHT IS ENERGY AFFAIRS MINISTER GEORGE BARTLETT. THE NEW PETROL PRICE **INCREASE**, HOW DID YOU ARRIVE AT SEVEN CENTS A LITRE?

WELL, JOHN--ONE MUST CONSIDER THE FUEL LEVY, THE "LANDED COST," WHOLESALE AND RETAIL MARGINS ... AND THE EQUALISATION FUND.

I HAVE **NO IDEA** WHAT YOU'RE TALKING ABOUT.

NEITHER DO I. BUT IF I TOLD YOU I THREW A DART AND IT LANDED ON SEVEN CENTS, YOU'D **REALLY** BE UPSET.

OOPS.

MY GUEST TONIGHT IS ENERGY AFFAIRS MINISTER GEORGE BARTLETT--THE MAN **RESPONSIBLE** FOR THE NEW PETROL PRICE INCREASE.

MINISTER... A GREAT MANY MOTORISTS WOULD LOVE TO GET **EVEN** WITH YOU.

I KNOW. THAT'S WHY BEFORE COMING ON THIS SHOW I INSISTED THAT MY VOICE AND IMAGE BE ELECTRONICALLY ALTERED.

YES. WELL, ... MINISTER... WE DECIDED **NOT** TO DO THAT.

WHAT?!

I OWN A CAR TOO, YOU PETROL PIRATE! VIEWERS! MEMORISE THIS MAN'S FACE!

HEY--TURN OFF THAT CAMERA!

17

MADAM & Eve

BY S. FRANCIS, H. DUGMORE & RICO

MADAM! LOOK -- THE CARTOON PANELS ARE ERODING!

YOU'RE RIGHT! THEY'RE COMING APART!

IT'S THE WEEKLY MAIL EDITORS! THEY KEEP CHANGING THE LAYOUT!

AND EVERY TIME THEY MOVE US, THE PANELS WEAKEN.

WHY CAN'T THESE GUYS MAKE UP THEIR MINDS!?

IT'S THE PRICE OF PROGRESS, EVE. THE NEW IMPROVED LOOK OF THE WEEKLY MAIL & GUARDIAN.

I'M TELLING YOU MADAM, THE PANELS CAN'T TAKE MUCH MORE OF THIS WEAR AND TEAR!

SHH! WHAT'S THAT NOISE?

RUMBLE!!

MADAM! WATCH OUT FOR THAT FALLING COLUMN!!

G-GO AHEAD, EVE... SAVE YOURSELF!

DON'T WORRY MADAM! I'VE GOT YOU!

LOOK OUT! INK FLOOD !!

AAAAAH!!

MADAM !?

EVE!

...ZONKER ?! FROM DOONESBURY ?!?

WOW! WHAT A TRIP!! WHAT PAGE AM I ON?

19

EVE...THIS IS SO EXCITING! MY SON ERIC'S PLAYING ROMEO IN A UNIVERSITY THEATRE PRODUCTION!

I CAN HARDLY WAIT TO SEE THE GIRL WHO PLAYS JULIET! ERIC TELLS ME THEY'VE BEEN SERIOUSLY **DATING**!

HARK! WHAT LIGHT THROUGH YONDER WINDOW BREAKS?

ROMEO!

A BLACK JULIET. INTERESTING INTERPRETATION.

HI MOM! YOU REMEMBER LIZEKA, MY GIRLFRIEND FROM UNIVERSITY?

YES...

GREAT NEWS, MOM. WE'RE MOVING IN TOGETHER!

ODD. SHE SEEMS ALMOST... FROZEN.

MOM?
MOM!?!

MOM... I KNOW YOU'RE HAVING TROUBLE DEALING WITH MY RELATIONSHIP WITH LIZEKA.

DON'T BE SILLY. IT'S THE FURTHEST THING FROM MY MIND.

...CAN I GET YOU SOME WINE? WE HAVE WHITE OR BLACK.

RED. I MEAN WHITE OR RED.

SHE'S REALLY FREAKED OUT.

TOTALLY.

20

ERIC!--LIZEKA! DO YOU *REALISE* WHAT YOU'RE DOING?! THIS IS SOUTH AFRICA! A WHITE BOY AND A BLACK GIRL WILL *NEVER* BE ABLE TO HAVE A *NORMAL* RELATIONSHIP!!

I DON'T SEE "BLACK" OR "WHITE", MOM. I HAVE THE ABILITY TO LOOK *THROUGH* THE SKIN ... AND SEE THE PERSON ON THE INSIDE!

SO DOES *SUPERMAN!!* BUT HE STILL DATES LOIS LANE!!

... THIS IS GOING TO BE DIFFICULT.

© Rapid Phase Entertainment 1993

ERIC! ARE YOU TELLING ME, YOU'RE GOING TO *LIVE TOGETHER* WITH A GIRLFRIEND WHO'S BL... BLL... BLA...

ARE YOU TRYING TO SAY "BLACK" MOM?

SEE?!! I'M SO UPSET, I CAN'T EVEN *SAY* IT!

MOM! ... THIS IS THE *NEW* SOUTH AFRICA ... WHAT'S THE *BIG DEAL*?!

© Rapid Phase Entertainment 1993

WHAT!? YOU'RE *MOVING IN* WITH A BOY WHO'S WH... WHI... WHI...

MADAM & EVE

BY S. FRANCIS, H. DUGMORE & RICO

...AND IF YOU JUST JOINED US, LISTENERS... STAY TUNED FOR A **SECRET** MESSAGE FROM NELSON MANDELA!

YES, YOU..!! WE'RE TALKING TO YOU!

THAT'S RIGHT, ALL YOU ANC SUPPORTERS OUT THERE... WE HAVE A **TOP-SECRET** MESSAGE FROM **NELSON MANDELA!**

SO TURN UP YOUR RADIO AND COME CLOSER...

THAT'S RIGHT...

CLOSER...

...AND BE CAREFUL! DON'T LET YOUR WHITE EMPLOYER HEAR THIS!

© Rapid Phase Entertainment - 1993

THAT'S RIGHT... PUT YOUR EAR TO THE SPEAKER...

...okay, is everyone here? Now listen carefully...

SMOKE ON THE WATER...

HEE-HEE! THAT GOT 'EM. HEY, PIET?

JA! THIS IS **RADIO PRETORIA**... FAR RIGHT ON YOUR RADIO DIAL!

MADAM & Eve

BY S. FRANCIS, H. DUGMORE & RICO.

...WE'D LIKE TO ANNOUNCE THAT THE 1993 **NOBEL PEACE PRIZE** GOES TO... NELSON MANDELA... AND F.W. DE KLERK!

WHAT MORE CAN WE SAY? IN THE SPIRIT OF **FAIR PLAY**, EVE AND I HAVE DECIDED TO IMPOSE OUR OWN "**SATIRE SANCTION**" ON THIS WEEK'S CARTOON.

THAT'S RIGHT, MADAM! FOR THE DURATION OF THIS STRIP, WE'LL REFRAIN FROM ANY **CHEAP SHOTS**, **LOW-BLOWS** OR **PUNCHLINES** AT THE EXPENSE OF OUR NATIONAL LEADERS.

OKAY, EVE. READY??

READY, MADAM.

GO!!

WHAT A TREMENDOUS HONOUR! MR. DE KLERK... MR. MANDELA -- HAVE YOU DECIDED WHAT YOU'LL DO WITH ALL THAT **MONEY**?

...PROBABLY HAIR IMPLANTS.

...AND I'VE ALWAYS WANTED A CADILLAC CONVERTIBLE.

OKAY. WE COULDN'T DO IT. SO SUE US.

© Rapid Phase Entertainment · 1993

25

MADAM-- ARE YOU SAYING THAT MANDELA AND DE KLERK HAVE TO **SHARE** THE NOBEL PEACE PRIZE MONEY??

YES, EVE. ...BUT DON'T WORRY, IT'S STILL AN INCREDIBLE HONOUR.

OKAY. NOW THAT MR. DE KLERK AND HIS ATTORNEYS ARE HERE, LET'S GET DOWN TO BUSINESS, GENTLEMEN.

MR. MANDELA PROPOSES A **SIXTY-FORTY** SPLIT.

WHAT!?

© Rapid Phase Entertainment · 1993

LET ME GET THIS STRAIGHT, MADAM. MANDELA AND DE KLERK HAVE TO **SHARE** THE NOBEL PEACE PRIZE?

IT'S NO BIG DEAL, EVE. EVEN AS WE SPEAK, THE MONEY'S BEING FAIRLY DIVIDED BY THEIR ATTORNEYS.

MR. MANDELA PROPOSES A SIXTY-FORTY SPLIT.

WHAT!? YOU'RE MAKING A **TRAVESTY** OF THE NOBEL PEACE PRIZE!

WHAT DO YOU THINK, MR. DE KLERK?

© Rapid Phase Entertainment · 1993

WAIT A MINUTE. WHO GETS THE SIXTY AND WHO GETS THE FORTY?

THIS IS RIDICULOUS, COUNCILLOR. HOW DO YOU FIGURE MR. MANDELA GETS **SIXTY** PERCENT OF THE NOBEL PRIZE MONEY WHILE MR. DE KLERK GETS ONLY **FORTY**?!

SIMPLE. MR. MANDELA HAS BEEN ON **TWICE** AS MANY "NEWSWEEK" AND "TIME" COVERS.

ALSO, HE'S BEEN FEATURED IN BIG HOLLYWOOD MOVIES LIKE "SARAFINA" AND "MALCOLM X!"

© Rapid Phase Entertainment · 1993

HE HAS A POINT, SIR.

OKAY! SIXTY-FORTY! ...BUT I GET TO KEEP THE TROPHY!

29

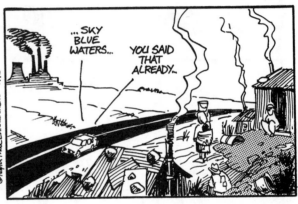

MADAM & EVE

BY S. FRANCIS, H. DUGMORE & RICO.

WELCOME TO THE SOUTH AFRICAN NATIONAL ANTHEM SONGWRITING COMPETITION! AND NOW... LET'S MEET OUR FIRST **FINALIST!** ...THAT PEOPLE'S POET FROM GRAHAMSTOWN... LET'S HEAR IT FOR...

...DOCTOR CHILL!!

ALRIGHT!!

...THEY'VE GOT TO BE KIDDING...

CLAP! CLAP! CLAP! CLAP! CLAP! CLAP! CLAP! CLAP! CLAP! CLAP! CLAP! CLAP!

...THE NEW SOUTH AFRICAN ANTHEM: A WORK IN PROGRESS.

BLUE WATERS SHINING ON OUR SHORE – MOUNTAIN TOPS AND FIELDS **GALORE** --

BULLETS FLY THROUGH GLASS AND BRICK -- TAXIS DRIVING THREE CARS **THICK** --

ELEPHANTS KILLED FOR IVORY **TUSK** -- WHILE WE DRINK OUR COFFEE, EAT OUR **RUSK** -- KILLIN' BLACKS AND FARMERS-- FRIEND AND **FOE** -- WHERE DID ALL THE TOURISTS GO?!

POLICE **DISGUISES** – NOBEL **PRIZES** -- POLITICIAN **COMPROMISES**! PETROL **PRICES** -- COFFIN **SIZES** -- THE UNITED NATIONS **OSTRACIZES**!!

WE MAY HAVE PROBLEMS – THIS IS **TRUE** -- BUT OTHER COUNTRIES ALSO DO! THAT'S OUR ANTHEM, I'VE STATED MY **CASE** -- SO PEACE ON EARTH...

...NOW GET OUT OF MY **FACE.**

THANK YOU.

...INTERESTING VIEWPOINT.

IF HE WINS, I'M EMIGRATING.

CLAP! CLAP! CLAP! CLAP! CLAP! CLAP! CLAP! CLAP! CLAP! CLAP! CLAP! CLAP!

34

BY THE WAY, MADAM... IF YOU GET ELECTED "MADAM OF THE YEAR", WHAT WILL MY NEW POST BE?

HUH?

IT'S A TRADITION IN POLITICS! WHEN PEOPLE HELP YOU WIN AN ELECTION, YOU'RE SUPPOSED TO REWARD THEM WITH A NEW JOB AND TITLE.

REALLY?

NO PROBLEM. IT JUST SO HAPPENS, I HAVE TWO IMPORTANT POSITIONS AVAILABLE NOW.

"AMBASSADOR TO LAUNDRY" AND "MINISTER OF IRONING" WASN'T EXACTLY WHAT I HAD IN MIND!!

I'M SORRY YOU LOST THE "MADAM OF THE YEAR" ELECTION, MADAM.

FORGET IT.

WHAT DID YOU DO WITH THE 300 LEFTOVER CAMPAIGN POSTERS?

I GAVE THEM AWAY TO THE HOMELESS.

GOOD, EVE. I JUST WANT TO PUT THIS WHOLE EXPERIENCE BEHIND ME AS SOON AS POSSIBLE... AND NEVER BE REMINDED OF IT AGAIN.

VOTE FOR GWEN ANDERSON
PLEASE HELP. NO JOB. NO FOOD. as bad as you think.

MADAM & Eve

BY S.FRANCIS, H.DUGMORE & RICO

HI THERE.

I SEE YOU STILL HAVE BRICKS UNDER YOUR BED.

EVE!! TOKOLOSHES!!

NOT AGAIN.

DON'T WORRY, WE'RE NOT HERE TO SCARE YOU. WE'RE HERE TO CAMPAIGN.

CAMPAIGN?!

YES. WE REPRESENT THE TP -- THE TOKOLOSHE PARTY.

OUR PLATFORM IS SIMPLE: VOTE FOR US OR WE TAKE YOU AWAY AT NIGHT.

...JUST KIDDING. ACTUALLY WE'RE KINDER, GENTLER TOKOLOSHES. ALL WE WANT IS OUR OWN TOKOLOSHE VOLKSTAAT, PROBABLY SOMEWHERE NEAR HOUGHTON.

ALSO, WE ASK THAT EVERY-ONE REMOVE THE BRICKS UNDER THEIR BEDS AND THAT THE 12TH OFFICIAL LANGUAGE BE "TOKOLOSHE."

WE'VE HAD LOTS OF BAD PRESS -- BUT READ MY LIPS: TOKOLOSHES CAN BE TRUSTED.

WELL, THANKS FOR YOUR TIME AND WE HOPE WE CAN COUNT ON YOUR SUPPORT. GOODNIGHT.

GREAT SCAM, SIR.

LET'S JUST HOPE THEY REMOVE THE BRICKS.

MADAM & Eve

BY S. FRANCIS, H. DUGMORE & RICO.

IN AN ATTEMPT TO DODGE THE MEDIA AND U.S. AUTHORITIES, **MICHAEL JACKSON** HAS CANCELLED HIS TOUR AND IS NOW IN **HIDING!** HE HAS LEFT SWITZERLAND AND IT IS RUMOURED JACKSON HAS NOW FLED TO A **THIRD WORLD COUNTRY.**

THEY'RE GETTING CLOSER, MICHAEL.

BOY. AM I IN TROUBLE, OR WHAT?!

THERE'S SOMEONE AT THE DOOR.

KNOCK! KNOCK!

THEY'VE FOUND ME! I KNEW IT!

IS HE HERE?

LIZ!!

LIZ! LIZ! LIZ! THANK GOODNESS!

HUSH, BABY. MAMA'S HERE.

REMEMBER... MICHAEL'S VERY TENSE. WHATEVER YOU DO, **DON'T SAY ANYTHING** TO **UPSET** HIM.

WE UNDERSTAND, MISS TAYLOR.

SO. UH, MICHAEL... HOW WAS YOUR FLIGHT? DID THEY SHOW A MOVIE?

YES... CHOKE "THE FUGITIVE."

©Rapid Phase Entertainment - 1993

NICE ONE, MADAM.

Sorry.

HEY--I KNOW! LET'S TELL A JOKE! LAUGHTER'S ALWAYS THE BEST MEDICINE!

MEDICINE! I ALMOST FORGOT! HAVE YOU SEEN MY TABLETS?

WAY TO GO **AGAIN** MADAM!

I'M SORRY! I'LL KILL MYSELF!

Oops.

LIZ!?!

THERE, THERE MY DEAR.

NEVER FAILS! EVERY DECEMBER THERE'S A MASS EXODUS FROM THIS CITY! EVERYONE JUST **TAKES OFF** FOR THE HOLIDAYS! WE'RE PROBABLY THE ONLY ONES **STILL HERE**, RIGHT EVE?

RIGHT, MADAM.

...RIGHT, MADAM.

...RIGHT, MADAM. CLICK

OKAY, YOU WIN. WE'LL GO ON HOLIDAY.

WE'RE ALMOST READY TO LEAVE FOR THE COAST, EVE! BRING YOUR BOARD!

...WRONG BOARD.

☆#@!!

MADAM & Eve

BY S. FRANCIS, H. DUGMORE & RICO

SPECIAL 7.25

‹DID YOU KNOW I'M A HAIRY BABOON?›

CIGARE...

‹BY THE WAY, I'M CRAZY IN THE HEAD.›

‹MY UNDERWEAR IS WAY TOO TIGHT.›

‹I EAT MY FOOD THROUGH MY NOSE.›

‹GOOD AFTERNOON. I'M A MAN WEARING A DRESS.›

‹HELLO. I LOOK LIKE A COW, DON'T I?›

‹YES. YOU DEFINITELY DO.›

‹SEE YOU LATER. MY FLABBY THIGHS MAKE A NOISE WHEN I WALK.›

...TEACHING MADAM MY LANGUAGE IS MORE FUN THAN EVEN I EXPECTED.

OOOO

©Rapid Phase Entertainment. 1993.

MADAM & Eve

BY S.FRANCIS, H.DUGMORE & RICO.

SPECIAL!

ONLY 116 SHOPPING DAYS LEFT UNTIL THE NEW SOUTH AFRICA.

JUST THINK, EVE... THE **NEW** SOUTH AFRICA IS ALMOST UPON US... WHILE THE **OLD** SOUTH AFRICA FADES INTO THE SUNSET... A DISTANT AND FORGOTTEN MEMORY...

ABOUT TIME.

SHOW A LITTLE RESPECT, EVE! SURE, THE OLD SOUTH AFRICA HAD ITS **PROBLEMS**, BUT IT WAS OUR WAY OF LIFE FOR MANY YEARS!

YOU'RE RIGHT, MADAM... MAYBE WE SHOULD CLOSE OUR EYES FOR A MOMENT OF SILENCE -- TO SOLEMNLY OBSERVE THE **PASSING** OF THE OLD SOUTH AFRICA.

GOOD IDEA, EVE.

© Rapid Phase Entertainment · 1993

THAT WASN'T SO BAD, WAS IT?

ACTUALLY, I QUITE ENJOYED IT.

EVE! COME LOOK AT THE SAND CASTLE I JUST BUILT!!

WOW-- THAT'S QUITE IMPRESSIVE, MADAM...

BUT... WHAT'S THAT LITTLE OUT-BUILDING OVER THERE?

THE MAID'S QUARTERS.

EVE! IT'S ALMOST TIME FOR MY CHRISTMAS PARTY! COME OUT AND LET'S SEE HOW YOU LOOK!

EVE!! THE GUESTS WILL BE ARRIVING ANY MINUTE!

REMEMBER. YOU'RE PAYING EXTRA FOR THIS.

THIS CHRISTMAS PARTY IS VERY IMPORTANT, EVE! I WANT EVERYTHING TO BE PERFECT!

DING! DONG! OKAY! THE FIRST GUESTS ARE HERE. AND FOR GOODNESS SAKE, ACT CHEERFUL!

WELL, IT'S HARD TO GET INTO THE CHRISTMAS SPIRIT WHEN YOU HAVE TO SERVE DRINKS DRESSED AS AN ELF!!

49

MADAM & Eve

BY S. FRANCIS, H. DUGMORE & RICO

WELL, EVERYONE'S GONE ON HOLIDAY, EVE. THE PLACE IS DESERTED! WE'RE PROBABLY THE ONLY ONES STILL HERE.

NOT QUITE, MADAM. LOOK!

YOU'RE RIGHT, EVE! THERE'S STILL SOMEONE OUT THERE!

INCREDIBLE!

C'MON -- GET A LIFE! GO OUT AND HAVE SOME FUN, INSTEAD OF SITTING AROUND READING A NEWSPAPER!

FORGET IT, MADAM -- LET'S GO!

WELL, S'LONG... WE'RE LEAVING NOW! HAPPY NEW YEAR! GET THE LIGHTS, EVE!

BYE.

CLICK!

WHAT ?!! YOU'RE STILL HERE ?!!

"SOME PEOPLE JUST CAN'T TAKE A HINT.

CLICK!

:SIGH: I GUESS WE HAVE TO STAY HERE ALSO... OKAY EVE -- GET THE TRIVIAL PURSUIT.

YES, MADAM.

RIGHT. TAKE THE DICE AND HERE'S YOUR FIRST QUESTION: "HOW MANY TEETH DOES AN ANTEATER HAVE?"

WELL ?!! COME ON -- WE'RE WAITING!

I KNEW WE SHOULD HAVE LEFT EARLIER.

©Rapid Phase Entertainment — 1993

LISTEN TO THIS, EVE...

ACCORDING TO THE NEWSPAPER THOUSANDS OF PEOPLE ACTUALLY GET DEPRESSED OVER THE HOLIDAYS.

...INCREDIBLE, ISN'T IT?

MADAM-- CAN I HAVE A RAISE?

NORMALLY, I'D SAY "NO WAY"...

BUT LUCKY FOR YOU, I MADE A NEW YEAR'S RESOLUTION TO BE KINDER, FRIENDLIER, AND MORE SUPPORTIVE

SO... YOU'RE GIVING ME A RAISE?

NO... BUT MY, THAT'S A LOVELY DRESS YOU'RE WEARING.

JUST THINK, MADAM! IT'S ALMOST NEW YEAR'S! WHEN EVERYONE CAN START OVER! TURN OVER A NEW LEAF!

FORGIVE ALL OUR PAST MISTAKES... WIPE THE SLATE CLEAN!

...WHAT'D YOU BREAK?

YOUR GOOD VASE.

53

TWEET!!

MORNING MADAM!!
HAPPY NEW YEAR!!

...SOME PEOPLE JUST DON'T APPRECIATE THE HOLIDAY SPIRIT!

© Rapid Phase Entertainment - 1993

ISN'T THIS GREAT, EVE? I'M SO GLAD I DIDN'T TAKE A LONG HOLIDAY. STAYING AT HOME GIVES US A CHANCE TO SPEND **QUALITY TIME** TOGETHER.

...GET TO KNOW EACH OTHER A LITTLE BETTER... NO POLITICS, NO PRETENSIONS...JUST YOU AND ME...

HOW MUCH TIME DO WE HAVE LEFT?

FIFTY-ONE HOURS, TWENTY-THREE MINUTES AND SEVEN SECONDS.

© Rapid Phase Entertainment - 1993,

SORRY I BROKE YOUR VASE, MADAM.

NO PROBLEM, EVE! MY NEW YEAR'S RESOLUTION IS TO **ALWAYS** REMAIN **CALM** AND NOT LET **ANYTHING** UPSET ME.

DID I MENTION...THE SINK'S CLOGGED?

NO PROBLEM.

THE PHONE BILL ARRIVED.

NO PROBLEM.

WE'RE OUT OF COFFEE.

NO PROBLEM.

...CAN YOU BELIEVE **WINNIE MANDELA** GOT RE-ELECTED?!

© Rapid Phase Entertainment - 1993

I GUESS EVERYONE HAS THEIR BREAKING POINT.

EVE! ARE YOU SWEEPING DIRT UNDER THE RUG AGAIN?!

EVE! HOW MANY TIMES HAVE I TOLD YOU **NOT** TO **SWEEP DIRT** UNDER THE **CARPET**?!

YOUR NEIGHBOUR WANTS TO KNOW IF YOU'VE SEEN HER CAT...

...AND AS THE TRIAL CONTINUES, THE DEFENDANT MAINTAINS SHE WAS **POSSESSED** BY A DEMON AND THEREFORE **NOT** RESPONSIBLE FOR HER ACTIONS...

...SOME PEOPLE WILL TRY **ANYTHING** TO GET OUT OF IRONING.

OUT OF ORDER?! ISN'T THERE AN **ATM** IN THIS AREA THAT **WORKS?!**

PSST. OVER HERE.

AUTOMATIC TELLAR MACHINE

SOMETIMES I'M GLAD I KEEP MY MONEY UNDER MY MATTRESS.

JUST KEEP WALKING.

OKAY, MADAM! THERE'S NO ONE IN SIGHT. READY?

READY.

QUICKLY! I ESTIMATE OUR WINDOW OF OPPORTUNITY AT THIRTY SECONDS!

HURRY MADAM! WE'RE RUNNING OUT OF TIME!

WAIT! I'M ALMOST DONE!... ...GOT IT!!

SIGH. ...IT'S SUCH AN EFFORT TO DRAW MONEY THESE DAYS.

KEEP ON YOUR TOES... WE'RE NOT OUT OF THE WOODS YET...

MADAM & Eve

BY S. FRANCIS, H. DUGMORE & RICO

ISN'T THIS **FUN**, EVE? I'VE ALWAYS WANTED TO TAKE ONE OF THESE TOURS!

TOWNSHIP TOURS

HI! WELCOME TO **TOWNSHIP TOURS**! I'M BOB AND I'LL BE YOUR TOUR GUIDE!

TODAY, WE'LL BE GOING THROUGH SEVERAL AREAS OF UNREST, SO HAVE YOUR CAMERAS READY!

HERE WE ARE! WE'RE ENTERING OUR FIRST "NO-GO" AREA!

AND LET ME STRESS FOR OUR FOREIGN TOURISTS...THIS IS A **REAL** TOWNSHIP AND THESE ARE **REAL** PEOPLE, NOT ACTORS!

UH-OH! WHAT'S THAT UP AHEAD!? IT'S...IT'S...A **BARRICADE**! ...LOOKS LIKE WE'LL HAVE TO TAKE A DETOUR BY THAT UNFRIENDLY HOSTEL!

...KEEP ON YOUR TOES, FOLKS... **LOOK OUT! A SNIPER!** THIRD FLOOR... SECOND WINDOW!!

TOWNSHIP TOURS

IT'S AN AK-47! HIT THE FLOOR!!

RATATATA!!

POW! PING!

PING

RATATATATA!

JUST KIDDING! DON'T WORRY, LADIES AND GENTLEMEN... OUR WINDOWS ARE THICK PLEXIGLASS AND COMPLETELY **BULLETPROOF**! HOW MANY WERE SCARED? RAISE YOUR HANDS!

...JUST A MOMENT! WE'RE IN LUCK! LOOK OUT YOUR RIGHT SIDE EVERYBODY! IT'S A **REAL** CAR HIJACKING ALREADY IN PROGRESS! IS THIS **EXCITING** OR WHAT!?

© Rapid Phase Entertainment - 1993

SEE? AND YOU DIDN'T WANT TO COME!

MADAM & Eve

BY S. FRANCIS, H. DUGMORE & RICO.

♪ "...DON'T BREAK MY HEART... MY ACHY-BREAKY HEART!" ♪

I LOVE THAT SONG! ...IF YOU'VE JUST JOINED US, THIS IS "RADIO MADAM & EVE" BROADCASTING FROM OUR HOUSE TO GREATER SOUTH AFRICA...

EVE AND I ARE GOING TO OPEN THE TELEPHONE LINES NOW! SO IF YOU WANT TO CHAT—HEY—GIVE US A CALL!

≈CLICK≈ ...HELLO?

HELLO. YOU'RE ON THE AIR!

WHAT'S YOUR NAME?

..BOB. I LIVE A FEW BLOCKS AWAY.

HI BOB! GOT A PROBLEM?

YEAH! YOU! I HAVE MY OWN RADIO STATION AND YOU'RE ON MY FREQUENCY! GET OFF THE AIR, YOU RADIO PIRATES!!

OH...AND I SUPPOSE YOU HAVE A REAL LICENSE?!

WELL...NO, BUT I WAS HERE FIRST! I'VE ALREADY BEEN BROADCASTING FOR ONE WHOLE WEEK!

≈CLICK≈ HEY—ALL OF YOU GET OFF THE AIR! I LIVE OVER ON FERN STREET... AND I'VE BEEN BROADCASTING FOR OVER TWO AND A HALF WEEKS!

WAIT A MINUTE. YOU SOUND FAMILIAR! WHAT STATION IS THIS?

"...RADIO KOOS VAN STADEN."

KOOS?... DON'T YOU ALSO OWN THE FISH MARKET DOWN THE STREET?

"...GWEN?! IS THAT YOU?

GWEN! YOU SHOULD COME BY THE SHOP! I'VE GOT SOME LOVELY FRESH HADDOCK!

REALLY?!

...THE POWER OF RADIO.

©Rapid Phase Entertainment – 1993

...IF YOU JUST JOINED US, THIS IS "RADIO MADAM & EVE"...BROADCASTING ILLEGALLY FROM OUR HOUSE! WE'VE OPENED UP THE TELEPHONE LINES. SO IF YOU WANT TO CHAT, CALL US!

...NOBODY'S CALLING. ISN'T ANYONE LISTENING? WHAT ARE THEY ALL DOING OUT THERE?!

Hi... THIS IS "RADIO BOB."

"RADIO PIET." IF YOU'VE JUST JOINED US...

THIS IS "RADIO XYZ"!

HI! THIS IS "RADIO VIVA"!

HI! THIS IS YOUR NEW LOCAL RADIO STATION, "RADIO MADAM & EVE"! GIVE US A CALL! OUR TELEPHONE LINE IS NOW OPEN!

HELLO?

:CLICK: HELLO, GWEN? IT'S MARGE. ...GUESS WHAT?! I JUST HAD MY BREASTS ENLARGED!

...UH, MARGE... YOU'RE ON THE AIR.

...I'M WHAT?!

REMEMBER, FOLKS! YOU HEARD IT HERE FIRST ON "RADIO MADAM & EVE"!

...I'M ON THE RADIO?!!!

...THIS IS "RADIO MADAM & EVE"! NOW LET'S CHECK OUT THE WEATHER IN "MADAM & EVE LAND"...

HOW FAR EXACTLY DOES "MADAM & EVE LAND" EXTEND?

...I'D SAY SOMEWHERE BETWEEN THE CORNER CAFÉ AND THE BUS STOP ONE BLOCK OVER.

THIS IS "RADIO MADAM & EVE." NOW LET'S GO TO EVE, OUR ROVING REPORTER WITH THE LATEST TRAFFIC UPDATE ...EVE?

THANKS, MADAM.

AND NOW, THE TRAFFIC REPORT: THERE'S A BLOCKED DRAIN TWO STREETS OVER, SO WATCH THOSE PUDDLES! ON FERN STREET, AVOID THE KIDS PLAYING CRICKET... AND, CROWDED CONDITIONS PERSIST AT THE CORNER CAFE, DUE TO LOTS OF PARKED CARS.

...AND THAT'S THE LOCAL TRAFFIC SITUATION! BACK TO YOU, MADAM!

...WE'VE JUST GOT TO GET A BIGGER TRANSMITTER...

© Rapid Phase Entertainment — 1994

...THIS IS "RADIO MADAM & EVE"! AND NOW, LET'S GO LIVE TO EVE SISULU FOR THIS EXCLUSIVE REPORT ON LOCAL NEWS! ...EVE?

THANKS, MADAM. I'M STANDING NEXT TO "FLUFFY"--A NEIGHBOUR'S DOG--WHO, MINUTES AGO, WAS ALMOST RUN OVER BY A PASSING CAR.

I BET YOU'RE LUCKY TO BE ALIVE, RIGHT, FLUFFY?

WOOF! WOOF!

© Rapid Phase Entertainment — 1994

A TRAGEDY NARROWLY AVOIDED. --THIS IS EVE SISULU FOR "MADAM & EVE NEWS." BACK TO YOU, MADAM.

...I'M HAVING TROUBLE ADAPTING TO THE **NEW SOUTH AFRICA**, DOCTOR.

...GO ON...

AFFIRMATIVE ACTION ... ...A NEW GOVERNMENT... A NEW CONSTITUTION ...

I MEAN ,...THINGS ARE CHANGING SO QUICKLY IN THIS COUNTRY, IT'S SCARY!

...YOU CAN SAY **THAT AGAIN!**

MRS. ANDERSON...YOUR REGULAR DOCTOR IS ON HOLIDAY. ARE YOU SURE YOU'RE NOT UNCOMFORTABLE BEING TREATED BY ME?

DEFINITELY NOT, DR. MABUZA.

...YOU'RE A TRAINED PSYCHIATRIST! THE COLOUR OF YOUR SKIN **DOESN'T MATTER** TO ME AT ALL! IT DIDN'T EVEN **CROSS MY MIND!**

GOOD. LET'S BEGIN, SHALL WE?

...ANYTHING YOU SAY, DR. BLACK.

..I MEAN DR. MABUZA.

...COMMON MISTAKE.

.. MAYBE I AM A LITTLE NERVOUS ABOUT THIS, DR. BLACK.

"MABUZA." IT'S DR. MABUZA.

OOPS. I DID IT AGAIN.

IT'S QUITE ALRIGHT. THAT'S WHAT WE PSYCHIATRISTS CALL A "FREUDIAN SLIP."

SORRY. ...COULD I USE THE WASHROOM BEFORE WE START?

BE MY GUEST.

GO DOWN THE HALL AND TURN WHITE.

70

BEFORE WE CONTINUE... I'M SENSING A LACK OF TRUST ON YOUR PART, MRS. ANDERSON.

OKAY!! YOU'RE RIGHT! I ADMIT IT!!

HOW CAN I TRUST A PSYCHIATRIST WHO "ROLLS THE BONES" TO MAKE A DIAGNOSIS!

...ROLL THE BONES?!

YES! WHAT'S THAT OVER ON YOUR DESK?!

THAT WAS MY LUNCH. KENTUCKY FRIED CHICKEN.

DR. MABUZA... YOU'RE SURE YOU DON'T "ROLL THE BONES" TO MAKE A DIAGNOSIS?

I'M A PSYCHIATRIST, MRS. ANDERSON!

WE ONLY USE THE MOST MODERN OF METHODS... HYPNOSIS... EXPERIMENTAL DRUGS... YEARS AND YEARS OF EXPENSIVE THERAPY...

... AND EVEN THEN, WE'RE NOT ABSOLUTELY SURE WE'LL BE ABLE TO HELP YOU.

GOOD. I WAS WORRIED THERE FOR A SECOND.

71

SHOULD I SCHEDULE ANOTHER SESSION FOR NEXT WEEK?

SORRY. I'M **BOOKED SOLID** FOR THREE MONTHS.

WHAT!?

I CAN'T HELP IT. THESE DAYS *EVERYBODY* WANTS TO BE TREATED BY A BLACK PSYCHIATRIST. IT'S VERY POLITICALLY CORRECT!

BUZZ!

YES?

FW DE KLERK ON LINE TWO, DOCTOR. HE SAYS HE'S DEPRESSED.

...WOULD YOU MIND IF I TAKE IT? WE'RE CLOSE TO A BREAKTHROUGH.

SURELY YOU CAN FIT ME IN *SOMETIME*, DOCTOR.

I'LL TRY, MRS. ANDERSON ...BUT BLACK PSYCHIATRISTS ARE VERY FASHIONABLE THESE DAYS.

FW'S STILL HOLDING, DOCTOR. HE SAYS HE'S GETTING MORE DEPRESSED.

I'LL BE RIGHT WITH HIM. WHAT'S THE REST OF THE DAY LOOK LIKE?

...YOU'VE GOT NELSON AT THREE O'CLOCK AND WINNIE AT FOUR.

WHAT?! YOU SCHEDULED THEM **BACK TO BACK**!?

...YOU *SEE* THE PRESSURE I'M UNDER?

I APOLOGISE FOR THE INTERRUPTION MRS. ANDERSON. PLEASE CONTINUE. YOU SAID YOU'VE BEEN FEELING DEPRESSED...

BUZZ

ROSE! I'M WITH A PATIENT!!

SORRY, DOCTOR. WINNIE'S ON LINE THREE. SHE SAYS SHE'S OUT OF MEDICATION.

I BETTER TAKE IT. THIS *COULD* AFFECT THE *WHOLE* COUNTRY.

MADAM & Eve

BY S. FRANCIS, H. DUGMORE & RICO.

AND NOW, IT'S TIME FOR THE ANC MISS SOUTH AFRICA PAGEANT!

...WITH THE TOKYO SEXWALE DANCERS! ...THE ANC YOUTH LEAGUE JUGGLERS! ...AND SPECIAL GUEST APPEARANCE BY NELSON MANDELA!!

...AND NOW, LADIES AND GENTLEMEN... PLEASE WELCOME YOUR HOSTS...WINNIE MANDELA AND PETER MOKABA!!

CLAP! CLAP! CLAP! CLAP! CLAP! CLAP!

WHAT AN EXCITING NIGHT! YOU CAN ALMOST FEEL THE ELECTRICITY! RIGHT, PETER?

SURE, WINNIE!

IT'S STRICTLY ONE JUDGE, ONE BALLOT, RIGHT, PETER?

THAT'S RIGHT, WINNIE. THE NEW MISS SOUTH AFRICA WILL BE JUDGED ON PERSONALITY, POISE AND POLITICAL CORRECTNESS!

AND HOW ABOUT THOSE PRIZES, PETER?!

THE NEW MISS SOUTH AFRICA WILL WIN A CASH AWARD OF 50,000 FINANCIAL RANDS, A SEAT ON THE NATIONAL ASSEMBLY AND A YEAR'S SUPPLY OF "BLACK LIKE ME" TOILETRIES!

AND HERE COME OUR FIFTY BEAUTIFUL CONTESTANTS!

JUST LOOK AT THEM TOYI-TOYI ACROSS THE STAGE!

STOMP! STOMP! STOMP! STOMP! STOMP! STOMP!

HI! I'M MISS KATLEHONG!

HI! I'M MISS SOWETO!

HI! I'M....

WHOAH! TOUGH BREAK! MISS PARKHURST HAS TRIPPED AND FALLEN!!

SHE'S GOT TO LOSE POINTS FOR THAT ONE, PETER!

SHE'LL NEVER MAKE THE SEMI-FINALS NOW!

RIGHT PETER-- AND BELIEVE ME, IT'S NOT EASY TO TOYI-TOYI IN A BATHING COSTUME AND HIGH HEELS!

WHAT A SHAME! AND SHE WAS OUR ONLY WHITE CONTESTANT!

AND WE'LL BE RIGHT BACK WITH MORE OF THE MISS SOUTH AFRICA PAGEANT AFTER THIS!

© Rapid Phase Entertainment - 1994

MADAM & Eve

BY S. FRANCIS, H. DUGMORE & RICO

BECOME POLITICALLY CORRECT ONLY R 10,00

LET ME GET THIS STRAIGHT. FOR TEN RAND YOU CAN MAKE ME POLITICALLY CORRECT?

...IN THE PRIVACY OF YOUR OWN HOME.

BECOME POLITICALLY CORRECT ONLY R 10,00

HA!

DON'T LAUGH, MADAM. USUALLY, IT TAKES YEARS TO ATTAIN TRUE POLITICAL CORRECTNESS...

BECOME POLITICALLY CO

BUT NOW, THANKS TO MY REVOLUTIONARY NEW METHOD, YOU TOO, CAN BECOME POLITICALLY CORRECT IN A MATTER OF SECONDS...

BECOME

...SECONDS?

THAT'S RIGHT! -- GUARANTEED TO MAKE YOU POLITICALLY CORRECT -- OR YOUR MONEY BACK!

BECOME

THIS I'VE GOT TO SEE! HERE'S MY TEN BUCKS.

BECOME POLITICALLY

OKAY... READY?

READY.

BECOM

PC!! HEAL!!

BECOME POLITICALLY CO ONLY R10,00

FEEL ANYTHING YET?

BECOME POLITICALLY CO ONLY R10,00

©Rapid Phase Entertainment — 1994

I... I THINK SO. ...YES! I DO!!

I KNEW I SHOULD'VE CHARGED TWENTY.

BECOME POLITICALLY COR ONLY R10,00

THE ANSWER IS...**YES**... TEN RAND PLEASE.

THE ANSWER IS...**NO**... TEN RAND PLEASE.

NOT "GINGERBREAD MAN." ..."GINGERBREAD **PERSON**." ...TEN RAND PLEASE.

© Rapid Phase Entertainment – 1994

...I'VE FOUND A NICHE IN THE MARKETPLACE.

POLITICALLY CORRECT ADVICE ONLY R 10.00

POLITICALLY CORRECT ADVICE ONLY R 10.00

YOU'VE GOT TO BE KIDDING.

POLITICALLY CORRECT ADVICE ONLY R 10.00

DO YOU HONESTLY THINK I SHOULD **PAY** YOU MONEY FOR ANSWERING A SIMPLE QUESTION?!

YES. I DO.

© Rapid Phase Entertainment – 1994

POLITICALLY

...YOU OWE ME TEN RAND.

POLITICALL

POLITICALLY CORRECT ADVICE ONLY R 10.00

OKAY. HERE'S MY TEN RAND.

WHAT'S YOUR QUESTION?

POLITICAL CORRECT ADVICE ONLY R 10.00

SHOULD I PAY MY MAID MORE MONEY EACH MONTH?

YES.

© Rapid Phase Entertainment – 1994

POLITICA CORREC ADVICE ONLY 10.00

NEXT!

POLITICALL CORRECT ADVICE ONLY 10.00

LOOK, EVE. IT'S BECOME ALMOST FASHIONABLE TO START YOUR OWN POLITICAL ORGANISATION!

RIGHT, MADAM! ...WHAT'S NEXT... "THE MADAM & EVE PARTY?"

THE MADAM & EVE PARTY!! EVE! YOU'RE A GENIUS!

OF COURSE, WE'LL NEED A MANIFESTO.

I'LL CHECK IF THERE'S ONE IN THE KITCHEN.

EVE...THIS IS A GREAT IDEA... FORMING THE "MADAM & EVE" POLITICAL PARTY!

JUST A MOMENT. WHAT'S OUR MANIFESTO?

OKAY... HOW ABOUT THIS...

"...MADAM & EVE... FOR FAIR, HONEST AND TRUSTWORTHY GOVERNMENT..."

CATCHY.

GOOD. AND KEEP SIGNING. WE'RE STILL SHORT FIVE HUNDRED SIGNATURES.

NEXT!! NUMBER 38!

RIGHT HERE! HERE'S OUR CHEQUE AND ALL THE SIGNATURES SUPPORTING THE "MADAM & EVE PARTY!"

CONGRATULATIONS. YOU ARE NOW AN OFFICIALLY REGISTERED NEW POLITICAL PARTY, APPEARING ON THE BALLOT.

SEE EVE? THE MADAM & EVE PARTY IS NOW AN IMPORTANT PART OF THE ELECTORAL PROCESS. A VIABLE POLITICAL ORGANISATION PLAYING A KEY ROLE IN OUR COUNTRY'S FUTURE!

NEXT! NUMBERS 39 AND 40! THE "DANCES WITH WOLVES PARTY" AND THE "TELLY FUN QUIZ PARTY!"

MADAM & Eve

BY S. FRANCIS, H. DUGMORE & RICO.

GOOD EVENING. MANY NEW POLITICAL ORGANISATIONS HAVE LITERALLY SPRUNG UP OVERNIGHT, HOPING TO PLAY A KEY ROLE IN THE UPCOMING ELECTION. NOW, LET'S MEET ONE OF THESE NEW ORGANISATIONS *DESPERATELY* SEEKING YOUR VOTE...

...THE MADAM & EVE PARTY.

MADAM...EVE... WHY DID YOU DECIDE TO FORM A NEW POLITICAL PARTY?

THE PEOPLE ARE **TIRED** OF LYING POLITICIANS! THEY WANT SOMEONE THEY CAN **TRUST**... SOMEONE WITH **INTEGRITY** AND **HONESTY.**

AND WHERE DID YOU TWO FIRST MEET?

ON ROBBEN ISLAND. WE SPENT YEARS THERE DURING THE STRUGGLE!

MADAM!!

AND **WHO** DO YOU COUNT AMONG YOUR SUPPORTERS?

LET'S SEE... WE'RE COUNTING ON THE MAID'S VOTE. THE MADAM'S VOTE. THE BLACK VOTE. THE WHITE VOTE. THE FEMINIST VOTE.

WHAT ABOUT MEN?

NOT YET. BUT WE'RE THINKING OF HIRING A **SEXY FEMALE CAMPAIGN MANAGER.**

MADAM!!

OOPS. THERE GO THE FEMINISTS.

MADAM...EVE... SOME CRITICS OF YOUR PARTY MIGHT SAY YOU HAVE NO POLITICAL EXPERIENCE.

NOT TRUE. WHO DO YOU THINK **ABOLISHED** APARTHEID?!

WAIT A MINUTE! *YOU* ABOLISHED APARTHEID?!

WELL, WE DON'T LIKE TO BRAG...

AND WE'LL BE RIGHT BACK WITH A CLOSING MESSAGE FROM THE MADAM & EVE PARTY.

EVE!! COME BACK!! WE'RE NOT FINISHED!!

©Rapid Phase Entertainment – 1994

RING RING! RING! RING! RING!

HELLO! HAVE YOU EVER CONSIDERED THE MANY BENEFITS OF TIME SHARE HOLIDAYS?!

OKAY, EVE. STARTING TODAY, I WANT YOU TO **SCREEN** ALL MY TELEPHONE CALLS.

...ME?!

YES, **YOU!!** IT'S ABOUT TIME YOU STARTED ACTING LIKE A **PROPER MAID** AROUND HERE!!

NOW LISTEN CAREFULLY! EVERY TIME THE TELEPHONE RINGS, **YOU** ANSWER IT **FIRST!** IF IT'S AN **IMPORTANT CALL,** THEN YOU BRING ME TO THE PHONE.

RING RING!

HELLO?!...MADAM'S RESIDENCE!

...**REALLY ?!!** YOU'RE **KIDDING!!**

...THAT'S **INCREDIBLE!**

OKAY... GIVE ME THE PHONE.

YOU'RE **SURE** YOU'RE NOT MAKING ALL THIS UP?!

I SAID GIVE ME THE TELE-PHONE!!

HOLD ON A SECOND. MADAM WANTS TO TALK TO YOU.

HELLO! HAVE YOU EVER CONSIDERED THE MANY BENEFITS OF TIMESHARE HOLIDAYS?!

MADAM & Eve

BY S. FRANCIS, H. DUGMORE & RICO.

"HI THERE."

EVE! THE TOKOLOSHES ARE BACK!

AGAIN? I THOUGHT THEY EMIGRATED.

WE TRIED! ENGLAND WAS TOO COLD... AND AUSTRALIA WAS TOO BORING.

SO... WE DECIDED TO STAY IN THE NEW SOUTH AFRICA!

SO... WHAT DO YOU WANT?

WE'RE TOKOLOSHES! YOU KNOW WHAT WE WANT! WE WANT TO CARRY SOMEBODY AWAY IN THE MIDDLE OF THE NIGHT. SOMEONE WHO WILL NEVER BE SEEN OR HEARD OF AGAIN!

BSST. BSST.

OKAY GUYS! LET'S GET OUT OF HERE!

LET'S GO! HURRY UP! MOVE IT!

WHAT DID YOU TELL THEM?

FELICIA MABUZA-SUTTLE'S ADDRESS.

MADAM & Eve

BY S.FRANCIS, H.DUGMORE & RICO.

I'VE ALWAYS SUSPECTED THAT WHENEVER I LEAVE THE HOUSE YOU INVITE YOUR FRIENDS OVER AND HAVE A PARTY!!

WELL? WHAT HAVE YOU GOT TO SAY FOR YOURSELF?

SURPRISE!! HAPPY BIRTHDAY TO YOU! ♪ ♫ HAPPY BIRTHDAY TO YOU! ♫ HAPPY BIRTHDAY DEAR MADAM...

NICE TRY! BUT IT'S NOT MY BIRTHDAY.

WE WISH YOU A MERRY CHRISTMAS! WE WISH YOU A MERRY CHRISTMAS! WE WISH YOU... ♫ ♪

...AND CHRISTMAS IS EIGHT MONTHS AWAY!!

ADMIT IT, EVE. I FINALLY CAUGHT YOU! IT TOOK ME A WHILE, BUT I FINALLY DID IT!! WHAT DO YOU SAY TO THAT?!

FOR SHE'S A JOLLY GOOD ♫ FELLOW! FOR SHE'S A JOLLY ♫ ♫ GOOD FEL-LOW!! ♫

MADAM & Eve

BY S. FRANCIS, H. DUGMORE & RICO.

WHAT'S GOING ON, MADAM?

AN EXPERIMENT, EVE. TO TRULY UNDERSTAND THE PLIGHT OF THE HOMELESS, I WANT TO BE A SQUATTER! TO SPEND ONE NIGHT AWAY FROM CIVILISATION -- EXPOSED TO THE ELEMENTS... WITHOUT SECURITY OR CREATURE COMFORTS!

...IN YOUR OWN BACKYARD?!

DO ME A FAVOUR. PLUG IN THE EXTENSION CORD. I WANT TO SEE IF THE ELECTRIC BLANKET WORKS.

ELECTRIC BLANKET?!

I'M SERIOUS ABOUT THIS, EVE. AWARENESS OF THE HOMELESS IS EXTREMELY IMPORTANT!

GWEN!

HI EVERYONE! BACK HERE!

GLAD YOU COULD MAKE IT! SET UP ANYWHERE!

WE BROUGHT EXTRA CARDBOARD. THIS "SQUATTER PARTY" IS A SMASHING IDEA!

"...SQUATTER PARTY?!"

OKAY... SO MAYBE I INVITED A FEW FRIENDS OVER TO SHARE THE AWARENESS.

MADAM! YOU'VE TURNED THIS INTO A TRENDY LIBERAL EVENT! BEING HOMELESS ISN'T LIKE CAMPING OUT WITH FRIENDS IN YOUR BACK YARD!! WHERE'S THE SUFFERING?! WHERE'S THE SACRIFICE?!

YOU'RE RIGHT.

ATTENTION EVERYONE!! AFTER OUR BRAAI, ELECTRIC HEATERS AND TV-SETS MUST BE SWITCHED OFF PROMPTLY AT NINE-O-CLOCK!!

AWWW!!

OKAY, NINE-THIRTY. BUT THAT'S FINAL!

YAY!!

THAT'S IT! I'M OUTTA HERE!

YOU CAN'T LEAVE! WHO'S GOING TO SERVE THE HOT CHOCOLATE AND MARSHMELLOWS?!

© Rapid Phase Entertainment -- 1994

MADAM & Eve

BY S. FRANCIS, H. DUGMORE & RICO.

MADAM--WHAT DOES "DEJA VU" MEAN?

IT'S WHEN YOU GET THE STRANGE FEELING YOU'VE DONE SOMETHING BEFORE.

DEJA VU.

OKAY EVE! IT'S TIME FOR OUR ANNUAL NEW YEAR'S RESOLUTIONS!

I CAN'T WAIT.

AND LISTEN TO THIS! EVERY TIME ONE OF US BREAKS OUR RESOLUTION WE HAVE TO PAY A FINE OF TEN RAND.

OKAY.

RIGHT. WHAT'S YOUR RESOLUTION?

I PROMISE TO WORK HARDER.

... AND I PROMISE NOT TO BE SO SELF-CENTERED AND EGOTISTICAL ... STARTING NOW!

THIS HAS GOTTA BE THE GREATEST IDEA I'VE EVER COME UP WITH!

... YOU OWE ME TEN RAND.

© Rapid Phase Entertainment 1993

MADAM & Eve

BY S. FRANCIS, H. DUGMORE & RICO

'TWAS THE NIGHT BEFORE CHRISTMAS... AND ALL THROUGH THE STATE... FATHER CHRISTMAS FLEW IN AS THE HOUR GREW LATE...

HE DECIDED TO VISIT THE CITY OF GOLD... AND SEE FOR HIMSELF THE NEW AND THE OLD...

HE WENT TO THE CENTRE THEY CALLED THE "WORLD TRADE," AND WATCHED AS GREAT PROGRESS WAS STEADILY MADE.

WENT TO CAPE TOWN AND DURBAN...PRETORIA TOO, HE EVEN ZOOMED OVER THE PLAINS OF KAROO.

HE VISITED LION PARKS, FINDING HIS WAY, (BUT WISELY HE DIDN'T GET OUT OF HIS SLEIGH.)

HE SAW PEOPLE AND DWELLINGS FROM WEST TO THE EAST, AND NOTICED THE VIOLENCE DRAMATICALLY CEASED...

WHAT HE SAW MADE HIM HAPPY, BUT BEFORE HE COULD LEAVE, HE DECIDED TO VISIT... YES, MADAM & EVE.

"THIS COUNTRY IS CHANGING, I MUST SAY I'M GLAD... GOT A LONG WAY TO GO, BUT THINGS AREN'T SO BAD."

"MATTER OF FACT, DOES IT SNOW HERE? NEVER! FORGET THE NORTH POLE-- I COULD STAY HERE FOREVER!!"

...AND THEY HEARD HIM REPEAT EVERY DAY, EVERY NIGHT...

©Rapid Phase Entertainment - 1993

MERRY CHRISTMAS TO ALL — AND TO ALL A GOOD NIGHT!

HEY EVE! MORE BEER!

94

EVE--WE'VE GOT TO LAUNCH THE MADAM & EVE PARTY WITH CREDIBILITY, AUTHORITY AND INTEGRITY!

MADAM...

WE NEED MEDIA COVERAGE! A POLITICAL PARTY DEPENDS ON IT!

BUT MADAM...

IN A FEW MINUTES JOURNALISTS ALL OVER THE COUNTRY WILL LEARN THAT THE MADAM & EVE PARTY IS A SERIOUS POLITICAL ORGANISATION, NOT TO BE TAKEN LIGHTLY!

© Rapid Phase Entertainment - 1994

WE'RE ALMOST OVER JOBURG. DON'T FORGET TO PULL THE RIPCORD.

LADIES AND GENTLEMEN OF THE PRESS--THANK YOU FOR COMING TO THE OFFICIAL LAUNCH OF THE MADAM & EVE PARTY!!

MADAM & EVE HAVE SUBSTANCE! THEY FOCUS ON REAL ISSUES! NO SLICK ANSWERS OR POLITICAL GIMMICKS!

MADAM & EVE HAVE AUTHORITY, INTEGRITY AND CREDIBILITY!

UH. WHERE ARE THEY?

RIGHT ABOVE YOU. WATCH OUT FOR THEIR DAY-GLO PARACHUTES!

As I said, ladies and gentlemen of the press, the Madam & Eve Political Party is a party with integrity...

...and they'll be parachuting down any minute.

...uh, there seems to be a slight delay...

Jump! We're over Joburg!

Okay! 500 bucks! That's my last offer!!

Hello? I want to speak to Mr. Mandela please. This is Gwen Anderson of the Madam & Eve Party.

The WHO ??!

The Madam & Eve Party!! We demand that Mr. Mandela and Mr. de Klerk debate us before a live TV audience!

Furthermore, I...

-CLICK!-

Hello?! ...Hello?!

They're scared of us.

© Rapid Phase Entertainment - 1994

MADAM & Eve

BY S. FRANCIS, H. DUGMORE & RICO.

EVE! I'M DONE WITH MY BREAKFAST!

ARE YOU GOING TO FINISH THAT TOAST?

EVE!! THERE'S A STRANGE BLACK MAN UNDER MY BED!!

ALL RIGHT! WHO'S UNDER THERE?!

IT'S LUCAS MANGOPE! PLEASE DON'T SHOOT!

LUCAS MANGOPE?!

SHHH! KEEP YOUR VOICE DOWN. I JUST NEED TO HIDE HERE A FEW DAYS UNTIL I CAN GO BACK TO BOPHUTHATSWANA.

MADAM... SOMEBODY SHOULD TELL THIS GUY HE DOESN'T HAVE A GOVERNMENT ANY MORE.

WE'VE BEEN TRYING TO. HE WON'T LISTEN.

WHO'S THAT?!

JUST MY CABINET MEMBERS. THEY'RE BEHIND THE CURTAIN. IGNORE THEM.

RIGHT! THAT DOES IT! EVERYONE OUT OF MY HOUSE!!

WHAT!? THIS IS TREASON! POLICE -- ARREST THESE WOMEN!!

NO WAY, SIR. WE'RE STAYING IN THE BATHROOM.

© Rapid Phase Entertainment—1994

99

HERE'S YOUR BREAKFAST, MOTHER ANDERSON. IF YOU WANT ANYTHING, JUST CALL ME.

THAT'S OKAY. I BROUGHT A **SERVANT'S** BELL FROM ENGLAND.

ONE TINKLE MEANS I WANT YOU. TWO TINKLES MEANS IT'S TEA TIME.

Tinkle. Tinkle.

Tinkle Tinkle Tinkle Tinkle Tinkle Tinkle

MOM--I'M GLAD YOU CAME TO VISIT...BUT YOU CAN'T BE THE CAMPAIGN MANAGER FOR THE MADAM & EVE PARTY!

WHY NOT?

YOU HAVE **NO** EXPERIENCE IN POLITICS!

WRONG! I CAMPAIGNED FOR WINSTON CHURCHILL IN 1945!

...DIDN'T HE **LOSE**?

YES! AND IF HE'D LISTENED TO ME, HE'D STILL BE IN OFFICE!

C'MON, EVE! LET MY MOTHER BE OUR CAMPAIGN MANAGER! WHAT DO WE HAVE TO LOSE?

...BESIDES THE ELECTION?

WHAT--DO I HAVE TO PAY YOU TO ALLOW MY OWN MOTHER TO WORK FOR US?!

MANDELA'S THE BLACK ONE, RIGHT?

...TWO HUNDRED AND TWENTY...TWO HUNDRED AND FORTY...TWO HUNDRED AND SIXTY...

© Rapid Phase Entertainment - 1994

100

Panel 1: I CAN'T **BELIEVE** I HAD TO PAY YOU **FOUR HUNDRED RAND** TO LET MY **OWN** MOTHER BE OUR CAMPAIGN MANAGER.

Panel 2: ...HOW'S IT GOING, MOM?

GOOD. I'VE BEEN STUDYING ALL THE **POLITICAL LEADERS** ON TV.

Panel 3: ...WHO'S THAT ATTRACTIVE **WHITE** MAN WITH THE **BEARD** AND **KHAKI UNIFORM**? HE SEEMS VERY NICE.

© Rapid Phase Entertainment – 1994

Panel 4: ...FOUR HUNDRED AND **TWENTY**... FOUR HUNDRED AND **THIRTY**... FOUR HUNDRED AND **SIXTY**...

Panel 5: IF I'M GOING TO BE YOUR CAMPAIGN MANAGER, I NEED TO KNOW MORE ABOUT THE **VOTING PUBLIC**...THEIR NEEDS...THEIR DREAMS... AND THEIR HOPES.

Panel 6: JUST SPEAK **CLEARLY** AND **SLOWLY** INTO THE TAPE RECORDER. ...READY?

READY.

Panel 7: TAPE NUMBER ONE: "EVERYTHING YOU ALWAYS WANTED TO KNOW ABOUT BLACK PEOPLE."

Panel 8: GO AHEAD. WE'RE ROLLING.

MADAM & Eve

BY S. FRANCIS, H. DUGMORE & RICO.

⟨WHO'S THE SLEEPING WHITE LADY?⟩ ⟨MADAM'S MOTHER... VISITING FROM ENGLAND.⟩

⟨JET LAG?⟩ ⟨...GIN AND TONICS.⟩

HERE--I'LL INTRODUCE YOU...MOTHER ANDERSON? HUH?

DON'T KILL ME! I'M FROM ENGLAND!!

IT'S ALRIGHT, MOTHER ANDERSON. THIS IS SOL. HE'S MY BOYFRIEND.

IT'S A PLEASURE. EVE--YOU TRANSLATE.

HELLO... HOW ARE YOU? I AM...FINE!

⟨"HELLO. HOW ARE YOU? I AM FINE."⟩

I COME... FROM FAR AWAY... ⟨SHE COMES FROM FAR AWAY.⟩

⟨LOOK, SHOULDN'T WE TELL HER I SPEAK ENGLISH?⟩ ⟨WE CAN, BUT IT TAKES ALL THE FUN OUT OF IT.⟩

I TRAVELLED ON A BIG SILVER BIRD!

⟨THAT'S A JET, RIGHT?⟩ EVE! I'M LISTENING TO THIS!

MADAM & EVE

BY S. FRANCIS, H. DUGMORE & RICO.

HI, GRANDMOTHER! THIS IS LIZEKA-- MY **FIANCÉ** FROM UNIVERSITY.

...DIDN'T I WRITE TO YOU ABOUT THIS?

MOTHER ANDERSON! I'VE HEARD SO **MUCH** ABOUT YOU!

ISN'T SHE **WONDERFUL**, GRANDMOTHER?

SHE'S **PERFECT!**

SHE IS?

OF COURSE! THIS IS A GREAT **POLITICAL COUP** FOR THE MADAM & EVE PARTY!

YOUR **OWN SON** GETS INVOLVED IN A **MULTI-RACIAL** RELATIONSHIP! THINK OF ALL THE VOTES YOU'LL GET! IT'S **BRILLIANT!!**

© Rapid Phase Entertainment — 1994

...SHE'S AN **ACTRESS,** RIGHT?

AND, IN OTHER NEWS, PRE-ELECTION HYSTERIA HAS GRIPPED THE COUNTRY. FEARING RIOTS AND DISRUPTION OF SERVICES, SOUTH AFRICANS ARE STOCKING UP ON TINNED GOODS AND CANDLES...

...CAN YOU **BELIEVE** HOW **PARANOID** EVERYONE'S GETTING?

MOM! COME OUT HERE! YOU'VE GOT TO SEE THIS!

TWO HUNDRED AND ONE... TWO HUNDRED AND TWO...

MOM! YOU ARE NOT BUYING MORE TINS OF BEANS!

IT'S A MATTER OF SURVIVAL.

SPECIAL $1.99

WHEN THE RIOTS START IN THIS COUNTRY, WE'LL BE ABLE TO BARRICADE OURSELVES IN THE BASEMENT, LIGHT CANDLES, AND EAT BEANS FOR THREE MONTHS.

10.99

IF THERE WAS EVER AN INCENTIVE FOR PEACE, THAT'S IT.

OKAY! I'M READY TO GO SHOPPING!

PLUNK!

@#☆6!!

MOM, IF I WERE YOU, I'D FORGET THE BULLET-PROOF VEST.

CLUNK!

107

MADAM & EVE

BY S. FRANCIS, H. DUGMORE & RICO.

MADAM, WHAT'S WRONG WITH YOUR MOTHER?

SHE'S WATCHING OUT FOR **SNIPERS**.

...IN A SUPER-MARKET?!

SOUTH AFRICA IS A **DANGEROUS** PLACE!

SHHH! LOOK OVER THERE! ON TOP OF AISLE FOUR...BY THE FROZEN PEAS!

WHERE? I DON'T SEE-- OW!!

WHAT'S WRONG, MADAM?!

CRIC!

...I PULLED MY BACK OUT! I CAN'T MOVE MY **NECK**!

STAY CALM, MADAM! I'LL CALL FOR HELP!

Special

Special 7.99

Special 7.99

G#☆G# SNIPERS!

SNIPERS?!

WHERE?!

SOMEBODY CALL THE POLICE!!

...AND IN OTHER NEWS, A BIZARRE SNIPER ATTACK ALLEGEDLY TOOK PLACE AT A LOCAL SUPERMARKET...

ISN'T THIS **EXCITING**!? WE'RE ALL ON TV!

© Rapid Phase Entertainment · 1994

MADAM & Eve

BY S.FRANCIS, H.DUGMORE & RICO.

...AND, WITH THE ELECTION FAST APPROACHING, **MANDELA**, **DE KLERK** AND **BUTHELEZI** HAVE AGREED TO ANOTHER LAST RESORT EMERGENCY MEETING THIS WEEK...ALTHOUGH THE LOCATION OF THE SUMMIT IS A CLOSELY GUARDED SECRET.

DING DONG!

QUICK, EVE--THEY'RE **HERE!** I'LL GET THE DOOR, YOU GET THE CHEESE DIP!!

GENTLEMEN. WELCOME TO THIS HISTORIC MEETING... UH, WHERE'S CHIEF BUTHELEZI?

DRIVING AROUND THE BLOCK. HE CAN'T **DECIDE** WHERE TO PARK.

NOW THAT EVERYONE'S HERE, I DON'T HAVE TO REMIND YOU THAT THE **FUTURE** OF SOUTH AFRICA DEPENDS ON TONIGHT'S OUTCOME.

MOM...YOU MAY BEGIN.

OKAY--HERE WE GO. DEUCES ARE WILD, JACKS OR BETTER TO OPEN! READ 'EM AND WEEP, GENTLEMEN.

HMMM.

HEH. HEH.

YES!

YOUR BET, MISTER MANDELA.

I'LL BET ONE CONSTITUTION REWRITE.

MISTER DE KLERK?

I'LL BET...A ONE WEEK LIFTING OF THE STATE OF EMERGENCY.

OVER TO YOU, CHIEF.

...I'LL **SEE** YOUR STATE OF EMERGENCY LIFT...AND **RAISE** YOU TWO ELECTION POSTPONEMENTS!

HE'S BLUFFING!

© Rapid Phase Entertainment-1994

HEY! STOP LOOKING AT MY CARDS!

I AM NOT!

LOUSY CHEAT!

MAYBE WE SHOULD'VE GONE WITH "OLD MAID."

109

HELLO, I'M TAKING A POLL. ARE YOU VOTING FOR THE MADAM & EVE PARTY?

UH, NO. NO. I'M NOT.

BONK!!

...WHO ARE YOU VOTING FOR?

THE MADAM & EVE PARTY!! THE MADAM & EVE PARTY!!

ANOTHER "UNDECIDED VOTER" SUCCESSFULLY SWAYED.

OKAY! TWENTY SECONDS TO GO! GRAB THOSE BEANS!!

MOVE! MOVE! MOVE!

...TEN SECONDS!! CARRY THOSE CANDLES!

...TIME'S UP! VERY SLOPPY! LET'S TRY IT AGAIN!

I REALLY HATE THESE ELECTION DRILLS.

MOM--YOU CAN'T STAY IN YOUR ROOM ALL DAY!

I'M NOT GOING OUTSIDE! THIS COUNTRY'S FULL OF COMMUNISTS!

WILL YOU STOP BEING SO PARANOID!? NEXT, YOU'LL BE SEEING COMMUNISTS UNDER YOUR BED!

WORKERS OF THE WORLD UNITE! YOU HAVE NOTHING TO LOSE BUT YOUR CHAINS!

YOU'RE NOT EXACTLY HELPING ME HERE, EVE!

...AND, AS A GESTURE OF RECONCILLIATION AND POLITICAL BONDING, I OFFER YOU MY HAND, MISTER DE KLERK.

A PLEASURE, MISTER MANDELA.

GOOD. ...NOW TAKE MY OTHER HAND.

...WOULD YOU CARE TO DANCE?

I'D LOVE TO.

♪ Strangers in the night... ♪

...I THINK THEY'RE TAKING THIS "BONDING" THING A BIT TOO FAR.

© Rapid Phase Entertainment — 1994

THIS IS IT, EVERYBODY! ELECTION WEEK!!

IT'S TIME TO MAKE HISTORY... TIME FOR A DEMOCRATIC NEW SOUTH AFRICA!

TIME TO STAND UP AND BE COUNTED!!

BUT FIRST, LET'S GET DOWN AND CHECK OUT THE WINDOWS...

© Rapid Phase Entertainment — 1994

AT LAST-- ELECTION DAY! IS EVERYONE READY?!

I JUST CAN'T WAIT TO WALK AMONG THE PEOPLE, TRAVEL TO A POLLING STATION, AND PROUDLY MAKE MY MARK FOR A NEW SOUTH AFRICA!

...YOU GO FIRST.

© Rapid Phase Entertainment — 1994

POLLING STATION

PSST! EVE -- CAN I BORROW YOUR PENCIL?

EVE WHO?

AAAAAH!!

SHH!!
SHH!
SHH!
SHH!

PSST! MADAM--I'M OVER HERE! THE VOTING BOOTH ON YOUR LEFT!

EVE...I NEED TO **BORROW** YOUR PENCIL.

WHY?

I ACCIDENTALLY BROKE THE POINT OF THE PENCIL THEY GAVE ME.

WELL...GO BACK AND GET **ANOTHER** ONE.

I CAN'T. I'M TOO **EMBARRASSED**. YOU'VE GOT TO LEND ME YOURS.

OKAY. FIFTY BUCKS.

WHAT?!

HEY--TAKE IT OR LEAVE IT.

OKAY. HERE.

I LOVE THIS NEW SOUTH AFRICA--FIVE SECONDS AFTER VOTING AND I'M **ALREADY** FIFTY BUCKS RICHER.

HI MADAM. ...ANYTHING NEW?

IT'S AN UNFOLDING **DRAMA**. VERY HARD TO PREDICT.

...WAITING FOR SOMETHING EXCITING TO HAPPEN...THAT'S THE WORST PART.

I KNOW... ELECTION RESULTS TAKE **FOREVER**.

ELECTION RESULTS? WHO'S TALKING ABOUT ELECTION RESULTS?!

AND NOW BACK TO "THE BOLD AND THE BEAUTIFUL..."

FINALLY.

AND NOW, THE SABC CONTINUES WITH OUR COMPREHENSIVE, **EASY** TO UNDERSTAND ELECTION COVERAGE --

INCIDENTALLY, THIS IS **CHANNEL ONE**, WHICH WILL CHANGE IN FOUR MINUTES TO CHANNEL TWO.

IN WHICH CASE, CHANNEL TWO BECOMES CHANNEL ONE.

UNLESS, YOU'RE ALREADY WATCHING CHANNEL TWO, WHICH BECOMES CHANNEL ONE. NOW AS FOR CHANNEL THREE ...

AND, CONTINUING WITH OUR ELECTION COVERAGE, I'M COMING TO YOU **LIVE** FROM SOCCER PARTY HEADQUARTERS...

COUGH! COUGH!

TELL ME ... AS THE CAMPAIGN MANAGER FOR THE SOCCER PARTY, DO YOU THINK YOUR PLATFORM TO **LEGALISE MARIJUANA** HURT YOUR CHANCES IN LAST MONTH'S ELECTION.

...WELL, ACTUALLY, I THINK THAT... WAIT A MINUTE! DID YOU SAY **LAST MONTH'S** ELECTION!?

HEY...EVERYBODY!! WE FORGOT TO VOTE!!

...BUMMER!

OH WOW!

DRAG MAN!

HEAVY!

118

MADAM & Eve

BY S. FRANCIS, H. DUGMORE & RICO

HERE THEY ARE, SIR. THE LAST BATCH OF BALLOTS... ALL COUNTED!

THANK YOU FOR VOLUNTEERING, LADIES. I'M ALMOST READY FOR THE **FINAL** TALLY.

CHIEF COUNTING OFFICER

WELL, GOODNIGHT SIR.

GOODNIGHT.

TWENTY ONE MILLION AND FORTY ONE... TWENTY ONE MILLION AND FORTY TWO...

THIS IS IT, EVE. THE IEC HAS WORKED ELEVEN MONTHS, TWENTY-FOUR HOURS A DAY FOR SEVEN MONTHS...

CHIEF COUNTING OFFICER

...MONITORING NINE PROVINCES AND FORTY MILLION VOTES.

...TWENTY ONE MILLION AND FORTY... UH...THREE...

...WITH ONE HUNDRED AND FIFTY THOUSAND VOTE COUNTERS AND FIFTEEN THOUSAND PEACE MONITORS... ALL AT A COST OF SEVEN HUNDRED AND FIFTY MILLION!

TWENTY ONE MILLION AND FORTY... UH...FORTY...

I'M JUST GLAD WE COULD HELP.

...FORTY...UH...

CHIEF COUNTING OFFICER

6#*%6☆!!

CHIEF COUNTING OFFICER

CHIEF COUNTING OFFICER

...ONE...TWO... THREE...

CHIEF COUNTING OFFICER

©Rapid Phase Entertainment – 1996

120

MADAM & Eve

BY S. FRANCIS, H. DUGMORE & RICO!

THIS IS SO **EXCITING**, MADAM! I CAN'T BELIEVE WE WERE INVITED TO **NELSON MANDELA'S CORONATION!**

THAT'S "**INAUGURATION**"!

DIDN'T I SAY THAT?

LOOK MADAM! A GIANT ICE SCULPTURE OF NELSON MANDELA'S HEAD!

YES...IT'S INCREDIBLE.

HELLO. WE'RE LOOKING FOR OUR SEATS. CAN YOU DIRECT US TO TABLE Z-103?

OF COURSE. YOU SEE THE LARGE DAIS WHERE NELSON MANDELA AND THE VIP'S SIT?

YES?

GOOD. TURN AROUND AND KEEP WALKING IN THE OTHER DIRECTION.

...HERE WE ARE MADAM. TABLE Z-103.

THIS IS OUTRAGEOUS! WE'RE ALL THE WAY IN THE **BACK**! TWO MORE METRES AND WE'D BE SITTING IN THE KITCHEN!

MANDELA LOOKS LIKE AN **ANT** FROM HERE! YOU CAN **HARDLY SEE ANYTHING!**

HERE. TRY MY BINOCULARS.

GEE, THANKS, WINNIE.

NO PROBLEM. ...BREADSTICKS ANYONE?

© Rapid Phase Entertainment – 1994

122

SO, SHOUT IT FROM THE ROOFTOPS...

WE'RE FREE AT LAST!

YOU HEAR THAT, MADAM?! ...FREE AT LAST!!

WELL DONE. ...DON'T FORGET TO DO THE DISHES.

© Rapid Phase Entertainment — 1994

THIS IS THE STRANGEST THING I EVER SAW! WHERE'D YOU GET IT, EVE?

I FOUND IT ON THE GRASS.

BE CAREFUL! IT COULD BE DANGEROUS!

IT DOES LOOK PRETTY SCARY!

MAYBE IT FELL FROM OUTER SPACE...

...SOME WEIRD ALIEN CULTURE...

AND, IN OTHER NEWS, BODYGUARDS ARE SEARCHING FOR WINNIE MANDELA'S HAT, WHICH BLEW OFF AFTER THE INAUGURATION...

© Rapid Phase Entertainment — 1994

AND THIS WEEK, NEW DEPUTY MINISTER WINNIE MANDELA CONTINUES HER REFRESHER COURSE IN ART, CULTURE AND SCIENCE...

OKAY, MRS. MANDELA. WE'VE COVERED "ART"; LET'S SWITCH TO SCIENCE.

FINE WITH ME.

WE'LL BEGIN WITH PHYSICS. IF A BODY IS THROWN OFF A BUILDING, DOES THE VELOCITY INCREASE OR DECREASE?

DON'T LOOK AT ME! I WAS IN BRANDFORT.

© Rapid Phase Entertainment — 1994

126

MADAM & Eve

BY S. FRANCIS, H. DUGMORE & RICO

EVE! THE MOST WONDERFUL PERSON IN THE WORLD! A PILLAR OF STRENGTH! A PARAGON OF VIRTUE! EVE IS THE GREATEST!

DON'T TELL ME...

IT'S ABOUT TIME I GET SOME PRAISE AROUND HERE.

YOU HIRED A PRAISE-SINGER?

IF THE PRESIDENT CAN HAVE ONE, SO CAN I. BESIDES... HE'S ONLY CHARGING ME FIFTY BUCKS FOR THE WHOLE DAY.

VACUUM! EVE IS THE GREATEST VACUUMER OF THEM ALL! SHE SUCKS UP EVERY LAST BIT OF DIRT!

DISHES! EVE IS THE GREATEST DISH-WASHER IN THE UNIVERSE! WITH THE SPEED OF AN EAGLE, SHE WIPES EVERY DISH!

WINDOWS! EVE IS A WASHER OF WINDOWS SUPREME! HER ANCESTORS WERE WASHERS OF WINDOWS SUPREME! FURTHERMORE...

THAT'S ENOUGH! TELL HIM I'LL PAY HIM THREE HUNDRED BUCKS IF HE KEEPS QUIET THE WHOLE DAY!

MADAM! SHE'S INCREDIBLY WISE AND GENEROUS!

WOW!...THREE HUNDRED BUCKS.

YOU'RE A GENIUS, COUSIN EVE.

SSHH! TEN FOR ME... TEN FOR YOU...

MR. PRESIDENT! IT'S GREAT TO SEE YOU!

YOU TOO! HOW COULD I FORGET MY FAVOURITE PRISON GUARD!

I COULDN'T HAVE **SURVIVED** ROBBEN ISLAND WITHOUT YOU! ...ESPECIALLY THE TIME YOU...YOU...

WHENEVER WE STRIP-SEARCHED YOU, I WAS THE ONE WHO GAVE YOU A BLANKET.

AND I'LL ALWAYS BE GRATEFUL, PIET.

IT'S "KOOS" SIR.

MARGE! GOOD TO SEE YOU! I'M SO GLAD YOU COULD COME TO MY PARTY!

MARGE! SHE IS GREAT! HER ANCESTORS ARE GREAT! VIVA MARGE! QUEEN OF THE PARTY ANIMALS!

I BLAME PRESIDENT MANDELA FOR THIS.

I DID IT, EVE! I HIRED MY OWN **PRAISE-SINGER**! WATCH THIS!

MADAM! SHE'S--

SHE'S A--UH--

...WHAT **ARE** YOUR GOOD POINTS? I NEED SOMETHING TO WORK WITH.

WHAT'S THIS?

IF YOU'RE GOING TO SING MY PRAISES, I TOOK THE LIBERTY OF WRITING A FEW THINGS DOWN.

MADAM! SHE'S KIND AND CONSIDERATE! SHE'S A WONDERFUL PERSON! SHE'S GENEROUS TO A FAULT! SHE'S --

...YOU BELIEVE ANY OF THIS?

YOU'VE GOT TO BE KIDDING.

...AND IN OTHER NEWS, WINNIE MANDELA HAS BEGUN HER TENURE AS THE NEW DEPUTY MINISTER OF ARTS AND CULTURE.

ALTHOUGH MRS. MANDELA SAID SHE HAS A THOROUGH KNOWLEDGE OF ART AND ART HISTORY...

SHE WILL, HOWEVER, BE TAKING A SMALL REFRESHER COURSE...

AND THIS IS ONE OF DALI'S FAMOUS WORKS.

WAIT A MINUTE! DALI TAMBO CAN PAINT??!

"PRESIDENT MANDELA."
I DEFINITELY LIKE THE
SOUND OF THAT.

BUT WHY STOP THERE?
..."ROYAL MONARCH
MANDELA... RULER OF
ALL OF AFRICA!"

NO. TOO LIMITING!
..."EXALTED MAJESTY
MANDELA, SUPREME
LEADER OF THE WORLD,
RULER OF THE
UNIVERSE AND --

THEY'RE
WAITING FOR
YOU IN THE
CONFERENCE
ROOM, WINNIE.

...BE
RIGHT
THERE.

CONTINUING OUR
INVESTIGATION INTO THE
SECRET KWAZULU
LAND DEAL...

...THE DAY BEFORE BEING
VOTED OUT OF OFFICE,
FW DE KLERK GAVE AWAY
1,2 MILLION HECTARES
OF LAND TO KING
GOODWILL ZWELITHINI...

SO FAR, HOWEVER, THE
CIRCUMSTANCES OF
THIS QUESTIONABLE
"GIFT" REMAIN A
MYSTERY...

FULL
HOUSE!
READ 'EM
AND WEEP,
CHIEF!

NOT SO
FAST,
BALDY.

AND, IN OTHER NEWS,
PRESIDENT MANDELA AND
DEPUTY PRESIDENT
DE KLERK MET TODAY TO
DISCUSS THE SECRET
KWAZULU LAND DEAL...

YOU WERE
IN A
POKER GAME
AND
LOST WHAT?!

UH, ONE
POINT TWO
MILLION
HECTARES
OF LAND.

WELL, I COULDN'T
JUST FOLD!
I HAD A
FULL HOUSE!!

THIS IS
MOST
REGRETTABLE.

HOW DO
YOU THINK
I FEEL?
THEY ALSO
GOT MY
CAR AND
ROLEX!

AND FOR THE LAST HOUR, PRESIDENT MANDELA AND DEPUTY PRESIDENT DE KLERK HAVE BEEN IN PRIVATE CONSULTATION TO DISCUSS THE RECENT KWAZULU LAND GIVEAWAY...

HOW COULD YOU LOSE 1,2 MILLION HECTARES IN A CARD GAME?!!

IT'S THAT BUTHELEZI! HE HAS A GREAT POKER FACE!

WHY DIDN'T YOU JUST FOLD?!

WHAT?!...AND NOT AT LEAST TRY AND WIN BACK THE PRESIDENTIAL MANSION?

YOU BET THE PRESIDENTIAL MANSION TOO?!

SORRY. YOU HAVE TO BE OUT BY TUESDAY.

©Rapid Phase Entertainment – 1994

OKAY, F.W. SHOW ME EXACTLY HOW YOU LOST 1,2 MILLION HECTARES OF STATE LAND IN A POKER GAME!

WELL, MR. PRESIDENT... I HAD A FULL HOUSE...

...AND THEN ...WHAM! CHIEF BUTHELEZI PULLED A ZULU FLUSH OUT OF NOWHERE!

A ZULU FLUSH?!!

YES. FIVE COMPLETELY DIFFERENT CARDS OF VARIOUS SUITS.

©Rapid Phase Entertainment – 1994

WHO TAUGHT YOU HOW TO PLAY POKER?!

CHIEF BUTHELEZI. ...IS HE LUCKY OR WHAT?!

MADAM & Eve

BY S. FRANCIS, H. DUGMORE & RICO.

EDITOR'S NOTE:

IN AN EFFORT TO EXPAND THEIR COMIC EMPIRE, THE AUTHORS ARE DEVELOPING SEVERAL NEW CARTOONS, UTILISING THE PROVEN MADAM & EVE FORMULA.

MEDELLIN & Eve

DON'T WORRY, MY FRIENDS, OUR COCAINE IS HIDDEN IN THE DUSTBIN. TRUST ME... IT'S VERY SAFE.

OOPS.

MANDELA & Eve

AND REMEMBER... AT THE END OF THE DEBATE, HOLD YOUR HAND OUT TO DE KLERK... LIKE THIS...

MADAM & CHRISTOPHER REEVE

FOR THE LAST TIME, DON'T JUMP! YOU'RE NOT REALLY SUPERMAN! YOU'RE AN ACTOR!

MADAM & Steve

GOOD! AND THIS TIME MORE EMOTION!

DIRECTOR

ADDAMS & Eve

DID YOU FINISH DUSTING THE LOUNGE YET, EVE?

PLEASE, MADAM! I ONLY HAVE THREE HANDS!

© Rapid Phase Entertainment - 1994

MADAM & Eve

BY S.FRANCIS, H.DUGMORE & RICO.

"DEAR EVE SISULU..."

"...AS YOU'VE PROBABLY HEARD, EVERYONE WHO VOTED FOR ME GETS A NEW BMW. HOPE YOU LIKE THE COLOUR. ENJOY! SIGNED... NELSON MANDELA."

VERY FUNNY, MADAM!!

SEE? I TOLD YOU SHE'D NEVER FALL FOR IT.

HAVE YOU BEGUN HANDING OUT THE UNOS AND MAZDAS YET?

NOT YET, MR. PRESIDENT. THERE'S THE SLIGHT PROBLEM OF WHO GETS THEM.

I TOLD YOU! EVERYONE WHO VOTED FOR ME GETS A NEW CAR!

...BUT THE BALLOTS WERE SECRET, SIR. HOW CAN WE TELL WHO ACTUALLY VOTED FOR YOU?

GOOD POINT... WE'LL JUST HAVE TO TRUST THE SOUTH AFRICAN PEOPLE. USE THE HONOUR SYSTEM.

NEXT!

E. TERREBLANCHE. I'LL TAKE THE LINO.

AND, BY POPULAR DEMAND, EVERYONE WHO VOTED FOR NELSON MANDELA, GETS A BRAND NEW REASONABLY-PRICED AUTOMOBILE...

ALSO, IN THE SPIRIT OF RECONCILLIATION, ANYONE WHO DIDN'T VOTE FOR NELSON MANDELA GETS A NEW TEN-SPEED BICYCLE...

...ANYONE WHO SPOILT THEIR PAPER WILL RECEIVE A FREE DINNER FOR TWO AT ANY MIKE'S KITCHEN...

© Rapid Phase Entertainment · 1994

AND, ANY RELATIVES VISITING FROM ENGLAND WHO WEREN'T ALLOWED TO VOTE, GET A NICE BOX OF CHOCOLATES.

...THAT'S ALL?!!

HI, ERIC. WHAT ARE YOU DOING HOME? HOW'S EVERYTHING AT UNIVERSITY?

WE'VE WON, MOM. THE STRUGGLE'S OVER.

THE GOVERNMENT OF NATIONAL UNITY IS FINALLY A REALITY! NO MORE PROTESTS AND DEMONSTRATIONS! NO MORE TEAR GAS! NO MORE RIOTS AND BOYCOTTS!

I'M SO DEPRESSED!

REBEL WITHOUT A CAUSE.

WHAT'S WRONG WITH ERIC?

HE'S HAVING TROUBLE ADJUSTING TO **UNIVERSITY LIFE** IN THE NEW SOUTH AFRICA.

IT'S SO **BORING** WITHOUT THE STRUGGLE! NO MORE DEMONSTRATIONS! NO MORE PROTESTS! WHY, THERE'S NOTHING LEFT TO DO AT UNIVERSITY NOW, EXCEPT... EXCEPT...

...GO TO CLASS!

...AND **STUDY.**

ONE STEP AT A TIME, MOM. I'VE GOT TO TAKE THIS SLOW.

DON'T YOU EVER MISS THE **STRUGGLE,** EVE?

NO, ERIC. ...BECAUSE FOR ME, THE STRUGGLE CONTINUES.

...IT **DOES**?!

OF COURSE! ...EVERY DAY IS **STILL** A STRUGGLE! CLEANING, COOKING, IRONING AND WASHING... IT'S ALL A STRUGGLE!

WOW. COULD I BE A PART OF IT?!

I'F YOU'D LIKE. YOU CAN START WITH THE WINDOWS.

AMANDLA!!

SOMETIMES I JUST CAN'T HELP MYSELF.

DON'T WORRY, ERIC. I'M SURE YOU AND YOUR FRIENDS WILL FIND SOMETHING TO PROTEST AND DEMONSTRATE AGAINST SOON.

IT'S HOPELESS, MOM.

IT'S THE **HONEYMOON PERIOD!** NO POLITICIAN IS GOING TO BE STUPID ENOUGH TO CAUSE A MAJOR SCANDAL, ESPECIALLY IN THE FIRST FEW MONTHS OF...

AND IN OTHER NEWS, MINISTER OF DEFENCE JOE MODISE HAS BEEN ACCUSED OF ATTEMPTING TO **CENSOR** THE MEDIA...

OH YE OF LITTLE FAITH.

THE **HONEYMOON'S OVER!**

JOE MODISE'S HERE TO SEE YOU, MISTER PRESIDENT.

IT'S ABOUT TIME! SEND HIM IN!

JOE-- YOU TRIED TO **CENSOR** THE MEDIA! ARE YOU **CRAZY**?!!

BUT MISTER PRESIDENT-- WE CAN'T JUST **ALLOW** NEWSPAPERS TO PRINT **WHATEVER** THEY WANT!!

WE HAVE TO, JOE. IT'S CALLED "FREEDOM OF THE PRESS."

WHAT A STUPID RULE! WHERE DID YOU HEAR **THAT**?!

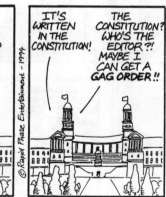

IT'S WRITTEN IN THE CONSTITUTION!

THE CONSTITUTION? WHO'S THE EDITOR?! MAYBE I CAN GET A GAG ORDER!!

137

MADAM & EVE

BY S. FRANCIS, H. DUGMORE & RICO.

FOR SALE
Real Estate

MADAM!!

SOLD ...AND GIVEN FREE TO WINNIE MANDELA

HELLO! I'M COLLECTING FOR WINNIE MANDELA!

WHAT?!!

ANY HOUSES YOU'D LIKE TO GIVE HER?

NO!

OH, COME ON! NOT EVEN A SMALL SUMMER COTTAGE SOMEWHERE YOU NEVER USE?

ABSOLUTELY NOT!!

OKAY. WHAT ABOUT A CAR?

NO! AND WHY SHOULD I GIVE WINNIE MANDELA A FREE GIFT?!!

WINNIE'S STRUGGLED SO MUCH! IT'S THE LEAST WE WHITE LIBERALS CAN DO TO SHOW OUR APPRECIATION.

ARE YOU CRAZY?!

YOU KNOW, IT'S PEOPLE LIKE YOU, THAT... THAT...

WHAT A LOVELY TEA SET! WINNIE WOULD JUST LOVE IT!

THAT DOES IT!! GET OUT OF MY HOUSE!!

...IS THAT AN ANTIQUE HAT STAND?

OUT!!

SLAM!!

...KIND OF GIVES NEW MEANING TO THE WORDS-- FREE MANDELA.

138

140

MADAM & Eve

BY S.FRANCIS, H.DUGMORE & RICO

HI MOM! IT'S UNIVERSITY BREAK, SO LIZEKA AND I THOUGHT WE'D COME BY AND SURPRISE YOU.

—MOM?

WE THOUGHT YOU'D WANT TO MEET LIZEKA'S BABY SISTER.

BABY SISTER?

SHAME. SHE'S SO CUTE.

HELLO.

LOOK MADAM. EVEN YOUR MOTHER'S TALKING TO HER!

THAT'S RIGHT, EVE. ...YOUNG OR OLD, BLACK OR WHITE...EVERYONE'S GETTING ALONG IN THE NEW SOUTH AFRICA.

...JIN AND TONICK?

RIGHT. AND BRING IT IN A TALL GLASS WITH LOTS OF ICE.

© Rapid Phase Entertainment · 1994

150

MADAM & Eve

BY S. FRANCIS, H. DUGMORE & RICO

THANKS FOR BABYSITTING LIZEKA'S LITTLE SISTER, MOM.

NO PROBLEM! BESIDES... EVEN MY MOTHER GETS ALONG WITH HER.

HERE'S YOUR GIN AND TONIC.

YOU FORGOT THE LEMON PEEL.

TELL ME A STORY.

SIGH.

OKAY. ONCE UPON A TIME THERE WERE THREE LITTLE PIGS. AND THEY LIVED IN...

A TOWN-SHIP?

ALL RIGHT, A TOWNSHIP. ANYWAY, THE FIRST LITTLE PIG BUILT A HOUSE OF TWIGS.

OH. A SQUATTER CAMP.

...THEN THE BIG BAD WOLF SAID, "LET ME IN!!" ...AND POUNDED ON THE DOOR!

WAS HE A POLICEMAN?

...AND HE SAID... I'M GOING TO BLOW YOUR HOUSE DOWN!!

A FORCED REMOVAL!! DID HE HAVE A BULLDOZER?!

...IT'S SO HARD TO TELL A FAIRY TALE IN THIS COUNTRY.

I'LL BET THEY DECLARED A STATE OF EMERGENCY!!

© Rapid Phase Entertainment - 1994

MADAM & Eve

BY S. FRANCIS, H. DUGMORE & RICO.

♪♫ JOIN OUR WORLD ON CCV! ♫♪

...OR DON'T JOIN IT. IT'S TOTALLY UP TO YOU.

COMING UP NEXT ON CCV... A CONTROVERSIAL DRAMA OF LIFE IN THE TOWNSHIPS, "THE LINE..."

UH... SORRY. DUE TO VIEWER RESPONSE, WE'RE CANCELLING THAT PROGRAM.

...UNLESS, YOU THINK WE SHOULDN'T. IT'S YOUR CALL.

HOWEVER, LIKE MANY OF OUR VIEWERS, WE AT CCV ARE OPPOSED TO CENSORSHIP!

...YOU ARE OPPOSED TO CENSORSHIP, AREN'T YOU? OF COURSE, IF YOU'RE NOT, WE COULD ALWAYS...

WILL YOU MAKE UP YOUR G☆#G MIND!!

WE'RE SORRY...YOU'RE ABSOLUTELY RIGHT! OKAY, WE'RE GOING TO SHOW IT NOW. SO GET READY... HERE COMES..."THE LINE"!

...ER, DID WE SAY "THE LINE"? WE MEANT "THE LION" AN EXCITING WILDLIFE ADVENTURE...

IN THE DENSE BUSH THE KING OF THE BEASTS STALKS HIS PREY.

CAN A TV-STATION HAVE A NERVOUS BREAKDOWN?

AND NOW, WE PRESENT "THE LINE"... A VERY CONTROVERSIAL TELEVISION DRAMA...

BUT FIRST... WE MUST **WARN** YOU THAT YOU MIGHT BE **RISKING** YOUR LIFE BY EVEN **VIEWING** THIS PROGRAM!! WE CANNOT BE HELD RESPONSIBLE! IN FACT, **CHANGE THE CHANNEL RIGHT NOW!!**

...THE SCENES IN THIS SHOW ARE **VERY** EXPLICIT! PLEASE, PLEASE, PLEASE **THINK** BEFORE YOU DECIDE TO WATCH!! ARE YOU **SURE** YOU REALLY WANT TO SEE THIS?!

WE HOPE WE'VE DISCOURAGED YOU. NOW HERE'S OUR PROGRAM...

YES!!

IN ADDITION TO "THE LINE," RADICAL GROUPS HAVE ISSUED AN UPDATED LIST OF TV SHOWS THAT WILL BE HUNTED DOWN AND KILLED...

"FULL HOUSE..." "MARRIED WITH CHILDREN" AND "COLUMBO..."

ALSO, THE FOLLOWING **ADVERTS** HAVE RECEIVED DEATH THREATS...

...THE BLUE ALIENS WHO RUN OUT OF PETROL...

HEY! I LOVE THAT ONE!

WELCOME BACK, MISTER PRESIDENT. HOW WAS YOUR CATARACT OPERATION?

WONDERFUL.

IN FACT, ACCORDING TO THE DOCTOR, MY EYES ARE IN GREAT SHAPE! NEARLY **PERFECT** VISION!

GLAD TO HEAR IT, SIR.

WHAT?

...GLAD TO HEAR IT, SIR.

PARDON ME?

GLAD TO HEAR IT, SIR!

MADAM & Eve

BY S. FRANCIS, H. DUGMORE & RICO

GREAT PARTY, MARGE. I DIDN'T REALISE YOU KNEW SO MANY BLACK PEOPLE!

I DON'T. THEY'RE RENTALS.

...RENTALS?

FROM "BLACKS 'R' US" ... AVAILABLE FOR PARTIES, WEDDINGS AND BAR MITZVAHS.

WHAT?! YOU **HIRED** TOKEN BLACK PEOPLE FOR YOUR PARTY?!

SHHH! THEY'RE PROFESSIONAL ACTORS! AND GETTING VERY WELL PAID, I MIGHT ADD.

EXCUSE ME, MARGE. I FORGOT WHO I AM. WHAT'S MY **MOTIVATION**?

YOU'RE A LAW SCHOOL PROFESSOR THAT I'VE KNOWN SINCE HIGH SCHOOL.

HEY-- I THOUGHT **I'M** PLAYING THE LAW PROFESSOR! I EVEN BROUGHT A **PIPE**!

ALRIGHT-- **YOU** CAN BE A RETURNING EXILE THAT'S NOW A MEMBER OF PARLIAMENT.

OKAY. I CAN WORK WITH THAT! GIVE ME A MINUTE TO GET IN CHARACTER.

YOU SHOULD BE ASHAMED, MARGE!... HOSTING A **PHONY** MULTI-RACIAL PARTY JUST TO IMPRESS YOUR RICH LIBERAL GUESTS!

... NOT TO MENTION THESE ACTORS! DON'T THEY HAVE ANY SELF-RESPECT?! SOME PEOPLE WILL DO **ANYTHING** FOR MONEY!!

...**EVE**?!! WHAT ARE **YOU** DOING HERE?!

EVE?? WHO IZ ZIS 'EVE'? I AM ZE FRENCH AMBASSADOR.

MADAM & Eve

BY S.FRANCIS, H.DUGMORE & RICO

...AND THAT'S WHAT **ANNOYS** MY MADAM THE MOST.

OKAY, WHO'S NEXT?

ME, ME!

MY TURN!

HERE'S A GOOD ONE. I ALWAYS WAIT UNTIL MY MADAM GETS **REALLY** COMFORTABLE, SITTING IN THE LOUNGE--

...AND THEN I START TO **VACUUM!**

HEEHEE! ME TOO!

HAHAHA! I DO THAT ALSO!

TRY THIS... "ACCIDENTALLY" LEAVE A TUBE OF NAPPY RASH CREAM BY THEIR TOOTH-BRUSH...

YOU MEAN... **NEVER FAILS!** THEY BRUSH THEIR TEETH WITH IT!

HAHAHAHA!

WHAT ABOUT PUTTING TOO MUCH STARCH IN THEIR UNDER-WEAR!!

YES! YES! OR RUN-NING A HOT TAP WHEN THEY TAKE A SHOWER?!

HA HA HEE HEE

HA HA HEE HEE HA!

HAHAHA! HEEHEE HAHA

SIGH

SIGH

SIGH.

EVE! CAN'T YOU DO A WASH PROPERLY?! I CAN'T FIND ANY OF MY LEFT SOCKS!!

BWA-HAHA! HAHAHA! HA! HA HA HA!

HEE-HEE! GOOD ONE! HEE-HEE! HAHA!

HAHAHA! I'VE GOT TO TRY THAT ONE! HEEHEEHEE!!

© Rapid Phase Entertainment - 1996

INTERESTING...

...ACCORDING TO THIS NEWSPAPER ARTICLE, A PERCENTAGE OF ALL BILTONG AND **PIES** IS ACTUALLY MADE WITH **HORSE MEAT.**

OF COURSE, MAYBE I SHOULD HAVE MENTIONED THAT A FEW MINUTES EARLIER.

LET ME GET THIS STRAIGHT, EVE. THESE MEAT PIES WE JUST ATE ... MIGHT CONTAIN **HORSE MEAT** ?!

YES. ACCORDING TO THIS NEWSPAPER ARTICLE.

NEIGHHH!
SNORT!
WHINNY!

WHOAH, BOY! WHOAH!

EVE! YOU FORGOT TO EMPTY THE DUSTBIN.

IT'S MY DAY OFF! CAN'T YOU TELL?

...NOT REALLY.

160

THIS **CRIME WAVE** IS INTOLERABLE! I REFUSE TO SIT HERE AND DO NOTHING WHILE CRIMINALS ACT WITH IMPUNITY!!

...WHILE **I'M** PRESIDENT, I WANT PEOPLE TO FEEL **SAFE** IN THEIR OWN HOMES! I WANT **BETTER** POLICE PROTECTION! I WANT--

...WAIT A MINUTE! DO I **KNOW** YOU?

...GIVE ME YOUR WALLET AND NO-ONE GETS HURT.

GOOD MORNING EVERYBODY! WHAT A BEAUTIFUL DAY! GREAT TO BE ALIVE, ISN'T IT?!

REMIND ME TO BUY HER SOME DE-CAFFEINATED COFFEE.

MADAM & Eve

BY S. FRANCIS, H. DUGMORE & RICO

AND, IN OTHER NEWS... A DOMESTIC WORKER, UNHAPPY WITH HER *LOW WAGES*, HAS ORGANISED A MASS DEMONSTRATION OUTSIDE THE HOUSE OF HER MADAM...

I'M WARNING YOU, EVE-- DON'T GET ANY IDEAS!

BUT, MADAM! I HAVEN'T HAD A WAGE INCREASE IN YEARS!

FINE! SINCE THIS IS THE NEW SOUTH AFRICA, WE'LL BE **DEMOCRATIC**.

ALL THOSE IN **FAVOUR** OF GIVING EVE MORE MONEY.. RAISE YOUR HAND.

...OPPOSED?

MOTION DEFEATED.

THAT'S NOT FAIR! I DEMAND A **RECOUNT!**

...ALL THOSE IN FAVOUR OF GIVING EVE MORE MONEY... RAISE YOUR HAND.

...MOM??

...**MOM?!!**

DECISION OVERTURNED!

I COULDN'T HELP IT. SHE SLIPPED ME TWENTY BUCKS.

I LOVE DEMOCRACY.

© Rapid / Phase Entertainment —1994

165

MADAM & Eve

BY S. FRANCIS, H. DUGMORE & RICO

AND IN OTHER NEWS, ANOTHER **ANC WEAPONS CACHE** WAS DISCOVERED TODAY. ACCORDING TO REPORTS, THESE SECRET WEAPON STOCKPILES HAVE BEEN TURNING UP IN UNEXPECTED PLACES...

EVE!!

HELLO. WE'RE FROM THE ANC. I UNDERSTAND YOU FOUND ONE OF OUR SECRET WEAPON CACHES.

THAT'S RIGHT.

OH, YES. I REMEMBER THIS HOUSE.

SORRY ABOUT THIS. WEAPONS ARE KIND OF LIKE **CAR-KEYS**. YOU ALWAYS FORGET WHERE YOU PUT THEM.

YOU MEAN -- YOU FORGOT THEY **WERE BURIED HERE?!**

WELL, TO TELL YOU THE TRUTH, SOMETIMES WHEN WE HID THEM, WE HAD A FEW DRINKS...

TOLD YOU WE SHOULD HAVE MADE A MAP.

WELL THANKS FOR CALLING US AND... ...UH-OH.

WHAT?

THESE ARE JUST THE GUNS! WHERE ARE THE ROCKET LAUNCHERS AND LIMPET MINES?

YOU MEAN THERE'S MORE?!!

...WAS THAT TENNIS COURT HERE TWO YEARS AGO?

NO,...WHY?

OKAY GUYS! GET THE JACKHAMMERS!!

NOW HOLD ON JUST A DARN MINUTE!!

MADAM & Eve

BY S. FRANCIS, H. DUGMORE & RICO

YOU SURE **LOVE** THOSE GIN AND TONICS!

AND IN OTHER NEWS... FOLLOWING THE SILVER-WARE SCANDAL, THE DEBATE OVER THE GOVERNMENT **GRAVY TRAIN** CONTINUES...

WHAT'S A "GRAVY TRAIN"?

IT'S A BIG TRAIN THAT POLITICIANS LIKE TO GET ON.

ISN'T IT HARD TO RIDE A TRAIN FULL OF GRAVY?

YOU'D BE SURPRISED HOW **EASY** IT IS.

DO PRESIDENT MANDELA AND MISTER DE KLERK RIDE THE GRAVY TRAIN?

USUALLY.

DOES WINNIE MANDELA?

OH YES. I'D SAY SHE'S A REGULAR PASSENGER.

WHY DON'T THEY TAKE A **GRAVY BOAT** OR A **GRAVY AERO-PLANE**? IT WOULD GO A LOT FASTER.

GOOD IDEA.

I BET THE GRAVY'S GETTING REALLY **DEEP** NOW!

YOU COULD DEFINITELY SAY THAT.

DO THE POLITICIANS **KNOW** THEY'RE ALL FULL OF GRAVY?

YES, BUT THEY'RE IN DENIAL.

MOM! I'M LISTENING TO THIS!

© Rapid Phase Entertainment – 1994

MADAM & Eve

BY S. FRANCIS, H. DUGMORE & RICO.

WELL, HERE IT IS... ANOTHER CHRISTMAS.

YES, EVE. WHERE DOES THE TIME GO?

REMEMBER THE GOOD OLD DAYS OF 1994?

1994?! I REMEMBER THAT! THE YEAR OF OUR FIRST ELECTION.

RIGHT. BEFORE THEY CLOSED OFF DURBAN AND MADE IT AN AFRIKANER VOLKSTAAT!

...BEFORE PETROL WAS 200 RAND A LITRE...

...BEFORE THEY ABOLISHED ALL ELECTIONS, INSTITUTED A MONARCHY AND CORONATED QUEEN WINNIE...

YES... AND BEFORE THE FOREIGN INVESTORS RUINED EVERYTHING...

WASN'T THAT ALSO RIGHT BEFORE THE GOLD RAN OUT?

YES. BEFORE THE COLLAPSE OF TELKOM AND THE NATIONALISATION OF EVERYTHING.

IT WAS ALSO BEFORE THE GOVERNMENT GAVE YOU MY HOUSE AND I STARTED WORKING FOR YOU.

AH YES... 1994... I REMEMBER IT JUST LIKE YESTERDAY.

CAN I HAVE A RAISE?

NOT A CHANCE.

...SOME THINGS NEVER CHANGE...